THE FIDIC CONDITIONS
Digest of contractual relationships and responsibilities

John G. Sawyer FRICS FCIOB MSE FCInstArb
C. Arthur Gillott BEng(Hons) CEng FICE

SECOND EDITION

 Thomas Telford, London

Published by Thomas Telford Ltd, Telford House, PO Box 101,
26–34 Old Street, London EC1P 1JH

First published 1981
Second edition 1985

British Library Cataloguing in Publication Data

Sawyer, John G.
    FIDIC, The: Conditions of, Digest
    of Contractual Relationships
    and Responsibilities.–2nd
    edition.
    1. International Federation of
    Consulting Engineers. Conditions
    of Contract (international)
    for works of civil engineering
    construction.
    2. Civil engineering—contracts
    and specification.
    I. Title   II. Gillott, C. A.
        624   TA180

ISBN: 0 7277 0248 3

Photoset, printed and bound in Great Britain by
REDWOOD BURN LIMITED
Trowbridge, Wiltshire

ACKNOWLEDGEMENTS

To our wives for their patience and understanding.

To all who contributed towards making this publication possible and for their efforts in correcting, editing, preparing and printing.

To the Fédération Internationale Des Ingénieurs-Conseils in the Hague for its kind permission to reproduce the contract document as an integral part of the Digest.

To those who have made known their views and opinions as to how the third edition of FIDIC Conditions of Contract (International) for Works of Civil Engineering Construction can be improved and their experiences which have contributed towards forming such views we are extremely grateful.

JOHN G. SAWYER
C. ARTHUR GILLOTT

FOREWORD

It should be noted that the Conditions of Contract (International) for Work of Civil Engineering Construction (FIDIC) are for works which will be measured and valued by using a Bill of Quantities and are not intended, without alteration, to cover lump-sum contracts or target/cost plus contracts or the like.

In applying the FIDIC Conditions of Contract, the order of precedence, insofar as those involved with any Enterprise are concerned is:

	Employer
	Contractor
supported by:	The Engineer and his
	Representatives
	Nominated Sub-Contractors
others involved:	Insurers
	Providers of Geological Data
by invitation:	Arbitrator.

By identifying the contractual relationships and responsibilities set out in the respective clauses in the document it is hoped that this Digest will provide a convenient means of reference to the student and practitioner as well as serving as a reminder that cash flow and construction can have a disturbing habit of suddenly stopping if the obligations and responsibilities each to the other are not fully and properly observed.

As the name implies a Digest is intended to reduce a subject into a systematic presentation of fact and information, to classify and summarise its contents so as to enable the reader to think over the information and arrange in the mind for further reference.

The inclusion of marginal references is purely for the purpose of easy identification and as such is incidental.

PREFACE TO SECOND EDITION

Encouraged by the success of the first edition the authors have prepared this second edition to enable a new section to be included which presents a commentary on selected clauses. The comments made cover at least two aspects of the particular clauses – one provides objective observations on selected clauses with recommendations for improvement or revision, the other offers notes on practical applications.

It is understood from international publications and FIDIC sources that efforts are being made to revise the existing FIDIC Conditions to make them more appropriate to modern requirements for international application and, at the same time, to remove those items which cause concern to the Employer and the Contractor and in which, in their present form, an apparent unfairness or ambiguity exists.

No attempt, beyond a few minor corrections, has been made to change the text of the original publication.

CONTENTS

INTRODUCTION

The manner in which any Contract and its Conditions become enforced is established through the Laws of the Land which govern the Contract and it is therefore of first and primary importance that the identification of the law applicable to the Contract is made clear as well as the ruling language where the Contract documents are written in more than one language.

So important is the identification of the language the Conditions require that a definition be made as to which is the ruling language where two or more *languages* are used within the Contract. The establishment of the ruling language *clause 5* determines that in any interpretation of the Conditions a second or other language is for convenience only and not to be considered authoritative if differences of translation arise.

It is good practice that, when a document is prepared in one language and translated into another, the second language version should be independently translated back into the original language as a check, then notwithstanding the high level of efficiency of the translators, a number of identifiable differences are often observed.

A word of caution about language would not go amiss at this juncture because when dealing with international business in foreign languages one must always be sure that the idea or concept perceived by each Party for a given word is the same for all. Because some people of different countries speak English very well one must never assume that their understanding of the English words and grammar is necessarily correct – indeed the same can apply when two people using their own natural language are communicating with each other.

Because of the numerous variations in legal philosophies throughout the world, the need cannot be over-emphasised for all Parties involved to possess an adequate understanding of the particular legal system according to which the *law* Contract is to be construed, and to be aware of the importance of receiving pro- *clause 5* fessional guidance on Statutes, Ordinances, National or Inter-State legal requirements which can override or influence the particular clauses contained within the FIDIC, or indeed any other, Conditions of Contract.

In using FIDIC Conditions of Contract there are many Parties who prefer to nominate the established Laws of England to govern the interpretation of the Contract, but it should be noted that the legal system in the country where any dispute is resolved (either through the courts or arbitration) may require the application of its own laws and negates such choice.

It should be noted that the attitudes of courts may vary in the interpretation of contracts – in some countries the courts will enforce a literal interpretation if this leads to a clear and unambiguous result whilst in other countries the courts will look more to the intentions of the Parties. The applicable law will also determine the extent to which the Parties are bound to carry out their contractual obligations. Under English law there is no concept of "force majeure" unless specifically incorporated within the contract – only the very restricted concept of "frustration" where a supervening event prevents performance by one of the Parties. On the other hand under systems based on the Code Napoleon the *force majeure* Parties to a contract are relieved of their obligations to the extent that they are prevented from performing them by a case of force majeure. Courts under such systems of law may, where exceptional circumstances render the performance of one Party's obligations so onerous as to incur heavy loss (but without rendering performance impossible) reduce the onerous obligations to a reasonable level of equity so required.

Once having recognised the importance of understanding the legal system which governs the Contract it is equally important for those involved with the Enterprise to understand in practical terms the nature of their responsibilities and liabilities, and the mode of conduct expected of them. Everybody involved within the Contract has an important part to play in order that the Enterprise might be completed successfully and this means the complete fulfilment of all their obligations each to the other.

The FIDIC document demands a system of communication which cannot be shortened or ignored without putting at risk the rights of any one Party to the Contract and therefore it is important to remember that when communications are required to be in writing this means precisely that, and in like manner, the giving of notices, instructions or certificates should follow the timing and procedures precisely as dictated by the Conditions of Contract, and in the detail required.

In the event of a dispute the legal representatives of all Parties will rely more than anything else upon written evidence, documents, and diaries, and if one Party has failed to fulfil its obligations properly in this respect, then its chances of success may be considerably reduced.

Those readers who are already familiar with both the fourth and the fifth editions of the Conditions of Contract issued by the British Institution of Civil Engineers will be well aware of points of similarity contained in Clauses in both of these ICE editions and in the FIDIC conditions – but they should not, because of their knowledge of the ICE Conditions, assume that FIDIC is equally applicable in usage – it is not.

FIDIC is a form of Contract not necessarily subject to the Laws of England; nor is the wording precisely the same as the ICE Conditions either in syntax or definition, and because of this the FIDIC Contract must be regarded separately in its own right and should be read and fully understood with these points in mind – in this context it should be noted that the FIDIC Conditions (third edition) has been translated into various languages such as German and Spanish.

1   THE CONTRACT

The FIDIC Conditions of Contract is a comprehensive document which contains general Conditions of Contract together with a Form of Tender and a Form of Agreement – all of which are essential parts of the Contract under which the Civil Engineering Works of the Enterprise are to be performed.

form of agreement
letter of acceptance
Within the Form of Agreement are details of other documents upon which the Contract is based and any arguments or disagreements arising under the Contract will rely principally upon these and no others. Probably the most important of these is the Letter of Acceptance from the Employer – because by this Letter the offer made by the Contractor is ipso facto written evidence that a Contract exists between both Parties.

letter of intent
Such a letter is different from Letters of Intent which generally indicate to the Contractor the intention of placing a Contract. If the intention is never implemented, and if the Contractor has expended money and effort without obtaining a separate assurance of payment for so doing, then the Contractor will have no basis upon which he can recover his money.

covering letter
If there are any difficulties or problems associated with any Enterprise concerning construction or finance, or indeed any other matter which is of such importance to the Contractor as to warrant special consideration, clarification or treatment, it is necessary for the Contractor to qualify the Tender to the extent suitable for the purpose. This is generally done in the form of an accompanying letter to which neither the Form of Tender nor the Form of Agreement in the FIDIC documents makes any specific reference.

Because of the absence of specific reference it is essential for the Contractor to safeguard his position to insert in both of these Forms a clear identification and reference to any letter accompanying his Tender if such a letter is to be an accepted and integral part of the Contract between the Employer and the Contractor.

law
Whatever new terms are to be added and whatever qualifications or changes are to be made to the Tender document the Contractor, before proposing other actions or modifications, should make certain that there are no overriding Statutes, Laws and Ordinances of the country to whose laws the Contract is subject, *clause 5* which might influence the precise application of the modifications he wishes to have agreed.

laws of England
If however the Contract is to be subject to the Laws of England then it is necessary for certain prerequisites to be observed before the Contract can be enforced by Law:

consideration
(1) Consideration – before an offer (Tender) can be accepted there must be an agreement by the Employer to give a consideration of sorts or payment made in exchange for having the work performed for him – this consideration is most essential in that if no consideration or payment is promised there is no legal Contract.

of same mind
(2) Of the same mind – this means that the two Parties to the Contract must be precisely of the same mind and to have agreed all major conditions of the Contract between them and about what the Contractor is offering and the Employer accepting.

acceptability
(3) Acceptability – there are a number of circumstances which prevent the two Parties entering into a legal Contract and it is therefore essential that each Party makes certain that the other Party is properly authorised to enter

into such a Contract and is acting within its limitations. It is also to be understood that a Contract signed by a Company which, or person who, has not the authority of that Company will receive no legal support – assumed authority outside recognised limitations in English Law is referred to as being ultra-vires.

ultra-vires

illegal enter-prise

Likewise people under certain ages, and those unfortunate enough to be classified as insane, are not permitted to enter into a Contract, nor is it possible for a Contractor to enter into a legal Contract for an illegal Enterprise.

(4) Writing – it is not necessary for a Contract to be in writing, although obviously for it to be in writing is the most desirable way of recording and conveying the intentions and responsibilities of the Parties to the Contract, each to the other. The Courts will generally accept the establishment of a Contract on a verbal basis but in this day and age of easy communication and documentation it is difficult to find a good reason why verbal Contracts need to exist at all. The prudent Contractor and Employer should always put into writing all matters of importance and should do so in such a way as to ensure that a response is required from the other Party – failure to receive a response to a proposal which requires agreement or acceptance cannot be claimed to be an acceptance of such a proposal.

In Contracts not subject to the Laws of England, but where the particular laws of the country involved are used, it is essential that such laws are clearly understood by both Parties. For example, it is no good believing that disputes under the Contract can remain unresolved indefinitely should Government legislation require that all disputes must be settled by a particular date in a statutory or religious calendar because if such an obligation is ignored a dispute could cease to exist after such date and be time-barred.

law

disputes

clause 5

clause 67

The FIDIC Conditions of Contract are divided into separate parts, each serving the purpose of collecting together clauses applicable to most forms of construction, be it land or marine work; they are drafted to allow the Employer to define any special arrangements or conditions which he requires to control effectively his function in the Enterprise, and also, to identify clearly whether he or the Contractor is to accept specified constructional or financial risks.

part I

Part I contains standardised clauses in respect of responsibilities, authorities, liabilities, each to the other, and in general terms gives a clear explanation of the nature and standards of the construction required but, more particularly, to the Contractor, provides specific definitions of the timing and the basis of the payment he is to receive.

Whilst the document makes reference to "payment by the Employer" it could be agreed between the two Parties to the Contract that in making payment "money" as such need not be involved – if they should agree that payment should be in the form of tonnes of cocoa beans or any other commodity this would be quite legal; likewise, if an indeterminate amount of money but positive in the form of a percentage of the toll-bridge takings, for example, is the consideration due to the Contractor for his efforts, then this also would be acceptable within the definition of the term "payment".

part II

Part II identifies again the selected Conditions already contained in Part I, for particular application. These clauses give positive identification to the name of the Employer and the Engineer and also the specific involvements of the Employer and a number of clarifications in respect of inter alia insurance, liquidated damages, nominated Sub-Contractors, certificates and payments.

It should be noted that Part II of the Conditions of Contract is referred to as an aide mémoire whereby it is intended to give indications only to various subject-matters listed but which sometimes require more detailed and precise consideration.

For the purpose of this Digest, the clauses which have been identified within Part II are examined and appropriate comments made – it should be understood, however, that these clauses are not exclusive and additional subjects may be selected and included as considered necessary when the Contract Documents are being prepared.

part III

dredging

Part III deals with dredging and reclamation work – whilst the FIDIC Conditions do not provide a particular section for those Enterprises concerned with Marine Work generally, it nevertheless identifies for particular application certain matters involved in dredging and reclamation work.

The Conditions applicable to dredging and reclamation work generally conform to those contained within the documents for other Works but with the difference that once the work has been taken over either wholly or in sections then the Contractor ceases to hold any responsibility for its maintenance.

geological data

Furthermore, the Employer is required to enlarge upon the geological soil specifications and, wherever possible, give information concerning navigation, environmental conditions and dumping places for dredged material, all of which forms the basis of the Tender with the Contractor being responsible for his own interpretation of the information given to him.   *clause 11*

physical con-ditions

Unforeseen physical conditions which arise, including climatic conditions encountered on site, permit the Contractor to be paid when such unforeseen conditions affect his work – it follows however that only those conditions which an experienced Contractor could not have reasonably foreseen would apply for additional payment. It would not be appropriate for the Contractor to claim for the effects of a monsoon, for example, knowing full well that such conditions were reasonably foreseeable and would affect his work anyway.   *clause 12*

It is noted that marine work in general is not given the same advantageous considerations as dredging and reclamation work, particularly bearing in mind that the vagaries of weather conditions and intensity of tide could be equally devastating to the construction of ports and jetties as they could be to the dredging of sea lanes and suchlike.

form of tender

form of agreement

The remaining parts of the document are the Form of Tender and Form of Agreement, and these need not be limited to the terms as listed therein because further terms could be added as necessary should circumstances or the wishes of the Employer or the Contractor make this desirable, but the content of any such Conditions once accepted cannot be modified other than by mutual agreement of the two Parties involved in the Contract.

singular/plural

In general it should be remembered always that the documents, and indeed the various Conditions within the documents, are to be read as each relating to the other irrespective of being singular or plural and one clause cannot be singled out for specific interpretation if conflicting with the intent or precise wording of other interrelated clauses.   *clause 1*

ambiguities

In the event of there being an ambiguity within the documents the Contract provides for the manner in which it shall be explained and adjusted and who is required to meet any extra costs which arise.   *clause 5*

Whilst a complete understanding of the Contract documents is extremely important it must also be recognised that the establishment and maintenance of a state of good relations between the Parties to the Contract is essential for the successful conclusion of any Enterprise and because of this it is worth making a concentrated effort at the beginning of the work phase to set up adequate but not too rigid acceptable procedures for communication and for all documentation to be coded under subject headings.

site meetings

Whilst it is common practice and worthy of encouragement to hold regular meetings at site level between the Engineer and the Contractor and also between the Contractor and the Sub-Contractors it is also sensible that the minutes or records of these meetings are written and agreed at the same time so that there can be no disputes later about what was agreed and discussed.

project manager, agent

Finally, from the Contractor's point of view it is desirable that an experienced Project Manager and Agent are engaged to act for him on site and to be given all the necessary authorities, responsibilities and financial resources to enable him to complete the works.   *clause 15*

The implementation of these recommendations should create a feeling of mutual respect between the Parties and improve the understanding of the various roles to be played by those involved in the construction of the Works bringing them together for the common purpose of achieving satisfactory completion.

2 THE EMPLOYER

An Enterprise usually arises from the need or desire for industrial or national development or for the purpose of speculation. Whether this is of a comparatively small financial status by a private speculator or entrepreneur or involves national authorities concerned with major projects of communications and development, the party requiring the work to be done is given the title of the "Employer".

Contrary to the opinions sometimes held by those who construct the Civil Engineering Works of the Enterprise and those who design them the most important person in the Contract is indeed the Employer – for it is his responsibility to provide the resources from which payments are made to the Contractor and others – it is he who has enabled the Enterprise to be conceived and wishes it to be completed, and in any language this means: no possibility of payment, no Enterprise.

Once having identified his construction requirements and objectives the Employer must embark upon a number of pre-Tender activities and these need to be carried out before inviting Tenders or bids from Contractors to execute the necessary Works of his Enterprise.

The Employer must first satisfy himself that he has adequate technical and financial capacity to honour his impending commitments under the Contract and this is immediately followed by the selection and appointment of an Engineer. To the Engineer he must entrust the overall responsibility for providing technical expertise to ensure the Civil Engineering Works of the Enterprise are properly designed and constructed and are suitable for the purpose for which they were intended.

The Employer does not appoint the Engineer under the FIDIC Conditions, nor is the Engineer a party to the Construction Contract. His appointment is covered by a Contract or Agreement which is entered into separately between the Engineer as a professional person or company and the Employer, the details of which are generally not disclosed to the Contractor. However, within the FIDIC Conditions of Contract the Employer is obliged to define any particular clauses according to which specific approval of the Employer is required before the Engineer can act on his behalf in relation to the Contract.

It is expected however that the Employer will ensure that his contract with his Engineer is such that the Engineer can, within such a contract, fulfil his obligations to the Parties to the Contract between the Employer and the Contractor for the Construction of the Works.

The Employer, in appointing the Engineer, undertakes to make payment for his services, but this does not necessarily make the Engineer an employee of the Employer in relation to the Construction Contract. His particular status as a quasi-judicial and independent person places the Engineer in a particular position which carries with it liabilities in their own right which are different from those which otherwise might have arisen as being an employee of the Employer.

*gineer employ-
ent*

The Engineer appointed for any contract governed by the FIDIC Conditions of Contract is not guaranteed employment for the duration of the Works of the Enterprise because the Employer, should he so wish, may appoint another Engineer – an individual, a firm of Consulting Engineers or a member of his own staff. Any Engineer named and appointed for the Works however would be expected to exercise his authorities and judgements impartially, fairly and beyond reproach.

In the event that the Engineer acted without impartiality the Contractor has the right to complain to the Employer and if not satisfied with the result, could, in England, take the matter to Court seeking to have the Engineer removed and another appointed in his place.

The Contract permits the Engineer to be removed at the discretion of the Employer and for the Employer to appoint a new Engineer – but should the Contractor have good reason to object to the nomination of the second Engineer selected by the Employer then he should do so.

engineer's representatives

The Employer is, at all times, responsible for ensuring that an Engineer is present and in control of the construction of the Works and may appoint the Engineer's Representatives should he so desire or leave such appointments to the Engineer.   *clause 1*

Once having appointed the Engineer, the Employer must have confidence in his technical and managerial expertise and thereafter recognise that he, the Employer, is not empowered nor required under the Conditions of Contract to interfere with, or undertake, those duties and responsibilities which he has delegated to the Engineer within the Contract.

The Engineer is required to act in many different capacities: as the Agent for the Employer in ordering Variations to the Works etc., as an independent expert and impartial mediator in the matters of valuation, extension of time, and initial arbitration disputes – his responsibilities to the Employer differ according to the capacity in which he is acting.

In major Enterprises sponsored by developing nations (and particularly with oil-producing countries) it is not inconsistent with modern-day practice for the Employer to retain control inter alia over the following matters:

Subletting any part of the Work
Variation orders
Certificate of Completion
Maintenance Certificate
Approval of Claims Settlements
Approval of new Rates.

original employer

Finally, in the event the original Employer ceases to exist the Contract does not terminate – the Contract would continue with the legal successors in title to the original Employer who in turn would become the Employer. Unless the Contractor consents, the successors are not permitted to transfer their responsibilities under the Contract to any assignee but are obliged to continue the Enterprise as the Employer or terminate the Contract. If the Employer wishes to assign the Contract to someone else he can only do this by agreement with the Contractor as the Conditions of Contract do not give him authority to do so as a right under the Contract.   *clause 1*

tendering

When the Engineer has issued the Contract documents and the Contractors are studying the proposed Works they often turn their attention to a number of specific items not necessarily directly concerned with the physical work required to be performed.

bond – tender

One of the first such items would be if the Employer required a Tender Bond to be submitted with the Tender – this Bond is intended to hold the Contractor to the offer he has made until such time as his or another Tender has been accepted and to ensure that the Contractor's bid is a serious one.

The amount of the Tender Bond is set sometimes to cover the anticipated difference between the lowest tenderer and the next one so that if the lowest bidder withdraws and forfeits the bond the amount recovered by the Employer thus covers such difference between the two lowest bids, so that, in effect, he can purchase the Works at the price of the lowest bid whilst accepting the next higher price.

Sometimes Contractors are handicapped by the existence of a Tender Bond because an unscrupulous Employer can threaten to call the bond if the Contractor is unwilling to extend the time period within which his bid is deemed to be valid and simultaneously to extend the time period of the bond. In these circumstances the Contractor may have to choose between paying the value of the Tender Bond to the guarantor if it is called or suffering the loss likely to be incurred if he is compelled to undertake a contract at a price which is insufficient because of the adverse effect of circumstances arising during the extended time within which he has been compelled to hold to his original Tender sum.

Form of tender

The Form of Tender obliges the Contractor to undertake to abide by his Tender for a given number of days but as no consideration is given for this undertaking and in the absence of a Tender Bond such an undertaking could possibly be ignored but to do so would be at the expense of the Contractor's good name in the industry.

guarantees

The terms of bonds or guarantees need to be watched very carefully. Sometimes there is no means of terminating a bond or guarantee because a termination date has been omitted or the wording is such that it is impossible to define when the obligation covered by the bond or guarantee has been fulfilled.

Bonds – advanced payment

Advance Payment Bonds or Guarantees, for example, should allow for the sum guaranteed to be reduced as the advance payment is repaid by set-off against monthly interim payments under the contract. Similarly Performance Bonds should allow for reductions in the amount guaranteed as and when parts of the Works are taken over by the Employer.

Bonds – performance

Performance Bonds, which are different from Tender Bonds, are required to be given by the Contractor as a guarantee that he will satisfactorily perform his Contract. The bond will be maintained throughout the Contract period, and for any extended time that may be granted, until completion of the maintenance period, and indeed until all liabilities of the Contractor to the Employer have been fulfilled.

clause 10

It is when the Contractor signs the Form of Tender that he formally commits himself to obtain the guarantee of an Insurance Company or a Bank by way of a Performance Bond but if, after becoming the successful bidder and his offer accepted, it is found that the Contractor cannot produce such a bond then the Contract is null and void and the Contractor may be liable to pay damages to the Employer.

Tender letter

Mobilisation

It is possibly because the Employer is given such a bond by the Contractor for due performance and is not required under the FIDIC Conditions to give any form of financial guarantee of payment to the Contractor that a number of Employers now find that the bidders include a Contractor's Tender Letter requiring an advance payment of considerable magnitude or that the Bills of Quantities are amended to contain items which include a large sum for mobilisation to be paid immediately after the Contract has been signed. This manoeuvre gives the Contractor partial coverage for the risk of the Employer defaulting on payment but needless to say when agreeing to provide advance payments, Employers in turn require Bonds to be provided by the Contractor equivalent to the amount of the advance payments.

Employer – default on payment

However, although this method of financial protection undoubtedly is becoming a practical way of satisfying the Contractor on a commercial basis, there exists already within the Contract, protection for the Contractor against default by the Employer once the work has started. In the event that the Employer fails to pay the Contractor any amount due under Certificate of the Engineer within thirty days after the same shall have become due under the terms of the Contract the Contractor has the right to terminate his employment under the Contract after giving fourteen days prior written notice to the Employer with a copy to the Engineer.

clause 69

Geological report

Possibly the next consideration of the Contractor is directed towards the general necessity in Civil Engineering Construction for every Site to be the subject of a geological investigation and for a report to be produced outlining the nature of the ground and the local hydrological and climatic conditions. It is unfortunate that many Employers seek to economise on this most important aspect of construction because it is from such information becoming available that the Engineer will design the Works. Similarly, the Contractor will use the same infor-

clause 11

mation to determine the particular techniques and plant requirements which he considers necessary for the construction of the Works.

Any report giving geological information must be made available to the Contractor and such information should be given to its fullest extent with no omissions. The Contractor is required to use this information in the preparation of his Tender and must therefore rely upon it being as comprehensive and as accurate as possible. If the Employer decides that the report should be edited before being issued – for Tender purposes – then he could risk being in breach of Contract should a claim or dispute arise during the course of construction concerning the accuracy of the geological date provided and if it be established that the editing changed the quality of the report in any way which reduced its value to the Contractor.

commencement of works

It is for the Employer to give early consideration to decide the Date of Commencement of the Works, and also, in conjunction with the Engineer, to determine the optimum contract period – this being the period in which the Works should be completed. Such a period is subject to any extensions granted (never a foreshortening) by reason of circumstances of Variations permitted under the Conditions of Contract.   *clause 41*

completion of works

bonus

In some instances the completion of the Works can be of such importance to an Employer that he will offer an incentive to the Contractor to finish the Works by a particular date or earlier than the time given in the original Contract – albeit taking into account adjustments to this time arising from entitlements within the Conditions of Contract. Such a payment is regarded as a bonus for completion   *clause 43*
and the amount and precise manner whereby a satisfactory achievement is to be measured so that bonus may be claimed should be specified in detail in the   *clause 47*
Tender Documents.

bonus

In particular, the Employer should note that if he relates the bonus payment strictly to the original Time for Completion together with such Extensions of Time as are granted by the Engineer then he is at risk by not taking the precaution of arranging to offset time saved when omissions to the Works are made by   *clause 47*
Variation Orders.

It should not escape notice that the Extension of Time which can be determined by the Engineer is in respect of additional or extra work only and does not   *clauses 43, 44*
make any allowance for omitted work to form part of the calculation.

bonus

Whilst Clause 44 concerns bonus to be paid upon a time basis there are obviously many other methods of bonus payments which can be made by the Employer and which are not necessarily related to time but evaluated on a target cost saving basis. Under such schemes the Contractor and Employer alike would   *clause 47*
receive the benefit of any cost saving in suitable proportions to be agreed.

liquidated damages

Contrary to certain opinions expressed it is fact that should the Contract contain a Liquidated Damages clause there is no necessity for a corresponding bonus clause. The two matters are completely separate and have no relationship   *clause 47*
one to the other.

possession of site

When considering the Works as a whole the Employer must take all necessary steps to ensure that the lands and the other places on which the permanent or temporary works designed by the Engineer are to be executed, or other lands and places provided by him for working space or other purposes, are sufficiently available   *clause 42*
for occupation by the Contractor at the appropriate times. A cautionary note – should the Contractor require other areas on which to establish his labour colonies, workshops, stores and offices then, unless these are situated within the portions of the Site handed over by the Employer or otherwise within the Site as defined, such other areas are outside the Site and payment for materials delivered and awaiting use within such areas may not qualify for payment as and when the Engineer determines the values of Interim Payments. If the Employer cannot give possession of the Site or portions thereof at the appropriate times then he must accept any additional costs incurred by the Contractor for such delays and whilst no written notice of handover by the Employer is specified there exists the implied action of written notice being given in that an authority for possession will accompany the Engineer's written order to commence.

The Employer undertakes to give the Contractor possession which allows the Contractor to move onto the Site to commence the Works, and having once given the Contractor possession, he is not in a position to eject the Contractor until the Works have been completed and the maintenance period has expired, unless the Contractor acts in breach of the Contract. He can, however, take over sections of the Works when substantially completed, but he may not enforce his presence by occupying any part of the Works until the Certificate of Completion for such part has been issued by the Engineer – to do so would again be in breach of the Contract.

commencement of work

clause 41

Should the Employer wish to enter the Works earlier than expected the Engineer could issue a Certificate of Completion without necessarily having received a request from the Contractor in respect of any part of the Permanent Works which has been substantially completed and passed any final test required even though the whole of the Works remain incomplete. If this happens the Employer becomes responsible for that part so taken over although the Contractor must complete any remaining outstanding work.

employer occupation of works

clause 48

It is becoming prevalent for either the Employer or the Contractor to insert into the Conditions a clause whereby the Employer accepts to pay an agreed rate of interest on outstanding payments to the Contractor in the event of failure by the Employer to pay the amounts due on an Interim Certificate of the Engineer at the time stated in the Contract.

payment – interest

clause 60

In practice this can often give little advantage to the Contractor in that it provides the Employer with the opportunity of not paying the amount certified without being immediately in breach of the Contract simply because there is a Contractual understanding between the Parties that if non-payment of an Engineer's Certificate occurs then an interest payment is to be made instead.

Obviously it would not be possible for such a practice to be maintained over a number of months without it becoming a critical problem and this means that should this situation continue for a sufficient length of time the Contractor should be able to claim in the Courts that the Employer, by his conduct, has shown his intention of rescinding the Contract.

In all it becomes a matter of commercial judgement but if the Contractor finds it impossible to continue on the basis of accepting interest only on outstanding debts he can claim default by the Employer for having failed to pay the amount due under a Certificate of the Engineer within the thirty days of the amount named therein becoming due.

The distinction is that the payment by the Employer of interest on outstanding debts is something between the Employer and the Contractor alone and is not part of the work performed and for which the Engineer is responsible for certifying payment – therefore, the failure to pay the Certificate of the Engineer by the Employer takes precedence over making only the interest payment and because of this the Contractor is entitled to terminate his employment under the Contract after giving the requisite number of days notice to the Employer (not to the Engineer) although he has an obligation to provide the Engineer with a copy of such notice.

It should also be recognised that in certain countries the payment of money for anything other than in return for something earned by trade or commerce is morally unacceptable and a Contractor may find that in asking for this interest payment an Employer becomes resentful. This is not necessarily caused by asking for the payment of the interest itself but because the Contractor has failed to show sufficient sympathy towards the Employer who is in the unfortunate predicament of having difficulty with his cash flow.

The Employer or the Engineer may wish to nominate someone other than the Contractor to undertake certain parts of the work it is necessary for them to agree the selection of Nominated Sub-Contractors by whom these works are to be undertaken.

nominated subcontractors

clause 59

A Provisional Sum will then be added to the Bill of Quantities covering the work to be done by such Nominated Sub-Contractors. If no Provisional Sum for such a nomination is included in the Bill of Quantities at the time of Tender, then

provisional sums

the Employer has no authority to subsequently nominate a Sub-Contractor *clause 58*
unless, of course, it is by mutual agreement with the Contractor.

Provisional Sums represent monies included in the Contract Price and Bills
of Quantities for work or contingencies for which at the time of Tender the Engineer did not possess sufficient information or had not made a positive decision
about the extent or necessity therefor. As part of the Contract Price, a Provisional
Sum is expected to be expended within the Contract Period – obviously, but not
necessarily, if the amount allowed is exceeded then a claim for an extension of the
Time for Completion could be made by the Contractor.

Provisional Sums can be used for work to be executed either by the Contractor or by a Nominated Sub-Contractor but, whereas the Contractor will be paid
as if the work arose from a Variation Order, the Nominated Sub-Contractor will
be paid only the amount stated as due by the Engineer. In such a case the Contractor is not involved in measurement or arguments about extra or varied work
but is obliged to produce as required by the Engineer any quotation, invoices,
vouchers and accounts for expenditure in respect of Provisional Sums.

If the Contractor decides to withhold any payment to be made by him to a
Nominated Sub-Contractor in respect of work performed by such a Nominated
Sub-Contractor then he is obliged to inform the Engineer in writing, stating the
reason for taking such action, and also to prove to the Engineer that he has likewise informed the Nominated Sub-Contractor; if he fails to do this and the Engineer certifies to the Employer that the Nominated Sub-Contractor should be paid,
nominated sub-contractor – non-payment then the Employer could pay the Nominated Sub-Contractor direct and deduct *clause 59*
the amount so paid from payments due to the Contractor as stated in the next
Certificate of the Engineer.

It is important to remember that the Contractor is in no position to argue
successfully that direction to him concerning payment to a Nominated Sub-Contractor makes the Nominated Sub-Contractor responsible to the Engineer
more so than towards the Contractor – the appointment of a Nominated Sub-Contractor could be one of personal selection by the Employer or the Engineer
and recognised by the Contractor when signing the contract.

Likewise, unless the Contractor raises reasonable objections against such a
Sub-Contractor at the time of nomination or unless he could not get the Nominated Sub-Contractor to enter into a Sub-Contract under the same conditions
nominated sub-contractor – objection which the Contractor has entered into with the Employer then he must accept *clause 59*
such nominations as made by the Employer or the Engineer.

There can be occasions when the use of a Provisional Sum is directly
involved with matters of design or specification for part of the Permanent Works
and includes any equipment or plant to be incorporated therein; it is however
provisional sums – involving design necessary for such requirements to be stated specifically in the Contract and likewise to be included in any Sub-Contract Agreement which the Contractor enters *clause 58*
into upon the direction of the Engineer.

The Nominated Sub-Contractor on his part must accept that in providing
such services as may be required and are covered by any Provisional Sum he will
nominated sub-contractor – indemnity of contractor indemnify the Contractor against all claims, proceedings, damages, costs,
charges and expenses of whatever nature arising out of or in connection with any
failure on his part to perform his obligations or fulfil any of his liabilities. *clause 59*

There can be occasions when the work performed by a Nominated Sub-Contractor under a Provisional Sum will be in respect of works to be executed, or
goods, materials or services to be supplied by him, which have an ongoing obligation which extends beyond the date of issue of the Maintenance Certificate.

If this situation arises then the Contractor should be requested by the
Employer to assign to him the benefit and cost of such an obligation for the unexpired duration – for this to be done it is necessary for the Contractor and the
Engineer to ensure when placing the order with the Nominated Sub-Contractor
that these arrangements affecting the Employer are properly recognised and included in the terms of the Sub-Contract.

Both parties to the Contract should be fully aware of the risks being taken by
each party separately or jointly and about what occurs when one or more of these

risks arise. With FIDIC Conditions of Contract being used on an international basis the Employer should pay particular attention to the "Excepted Risks" and study them with particular reference to his own environment or circumstances.

Nobody likes paying more than is necessary for anything they require, and in this matter the Employer is no exception with his Enterprise – hence he may elect to carry certain risks himself, possibly because he is more familiar with the country in which the works are being constructed and is better informed than the Contractor about the risks under review.

These risks are referred to as the Excepted Risks and have little to do with the construction of the Works unless they arise during the Construction period but, in electing to accept these risks himself, the Employer avoids receiving artificially high Tenders which could contain each Tendering Contractor's own individual assessment of the probability of any of these Excepted Risks occurring.

The Excepted Risks are generally concerned with war, hostilities and a number of lesser forms of aggravation down to commotion or disorder and also include the risks which might arise from radiation or nuclear activity, from the effects of pressure waves caused by aircraft as well as the cost of repair or making good which arises solely due to the Engineer's design of the Works (and it must be solely and not partially) or from use or occupation by the Employer.

The Employer also relieves the Contractor from liability arising from any operation of the forces of nature, which an experienced Contractor could not have foreseen, or reasonably could not make provision for or insure against. This is far from being as precise as could be desired in that some risks of this nature are insurable e.g. earthquakes, but depending upon the degree of probability of the risk materialising, the effect on the insurance premium to be paid can be very considerable. It is not easy to agree upon exactly what should be foreseen or otherwise and certainly it is difficult to determine the reasonableness of making some provision or not within the Tender Price for the effect of the forces of nature especially in countries where earthquakes, monsoons, hurricanes, typhoons and the like are regular annual occurrences.

There are obviously degrees of probability which affect the argument of liability when they do arise and, whilst it is recognised that earthquakes, tidal waves, typhoons, hurricane winds and other forms of inclement weather can occur during the Contract Period, it could be argued that such events are unforeseen if they appear out of historically recorded sequences, or if the frequency or intensity of such is demonstrated to be greater than experienced earlier and are therefore unforeseen for this Contract.

It is often only with hindsight that certain arguments succeed in defining precisely what should have been foreseen by a Contractor when tendering, and also whether the probability factor involving intensity or frequency of the occurrence of such natural conditions used by the Contractor in his tender could allow the Employer to condemn the Contractor for being negligent when building up his tender prices – but hindsight is not the criterion by which such judgements should be made.

The Contractor is not liable for damage arising from the Excepted Risks whilst executing the works and any remaining outstanding Permanent Works which were identified when the appropriate Completion Certificate was issued (or when part of the Work was taken into occupation or use by the Employer). This means that, up to the date of the Completion Certificate, the Contractor is indemnified by the Employer against the Excepted Risks for both Permanent and Temporary Works but after that date he is only protected for the Permanent Works, and is at risk for any Temporary Works which might remain in position and which have not been removed at that time. However he will remain indemnified by the Employer against the Excepted Risks for those Temporary Works which remain in position or are required and which are necessary to complete the outstanding Permanent Work he is obliged to do.

The Employer recognises the possibility of destruction or of damage to the Works (this would again include Temporary Works), and undertakes to indemnify the Contractor against claims proceedings, damages, costs, charges and

special risks

expenses whatsoever, which arise in the event of certain Special Risks occurring.

These Special Risks are war, hostilities, invasion, acts of enemies of the country in which the Works were being constructed, and of nuclear and pressure wave risks – much as described in the Clause dealing with the Excepted Risks, *clause 65* and insofar as it relates to the country in which the Works were being executed or maintained, for rebellion, revolution, insurrection, military or usurped power, civil war, or in respect of riot, commotion or disorder by any persons other than the employees of the Contractor or of his Sub-Contractors.

It is further seen that a war can be recognised to exist whether the formalities of declaration have been made or not, and also that it need not be within the particular country in which the Works are being constructed but could be elsewhere in the world and must be of such a nature that it financially or otherwise materially affects the execution of the Works.

If in the event any of the Works (including Temporary Works) are destroyed or damaged by reason of any of the Special Risks then the Contractor will be paid for any Permanent Works and for materials destroyed or damaged. He will if necessary replace or make good such destruction or damage to the extent required by the Engineer.

It is to be noted that the Special Risk clause does not contain any restriction or limitation of time up to the Completion Certificate as exists for the Excepted Risks and in fact effectively operates from the Date of Commencement until such time as the Contractor fulfils all his obligations.

If it is necessary to replace or make good after any destruction, then the Contractor will be paid on the basis of "Cost plus such Profit as the Engineer may consider reasonable".

If any materials which are near or in transit to the Site, or indeed any other property of the Contractor (this would therefore include Constructional Plant) used or intended to be used for the purpose of the Works (including Temporary Works), sustain damage or are destroyed, then the Contractor will be paid under this Clause. He will also recover any increased cost or cost incidental to the execution of the Work but not in respect of reconstructing work condemned under Clause 39.

war

If an outbreak of war occurs (and noting that this is now being referred to as a singular item for consideration and not including all of the other Special Risks) then the Employer but not the Contractor can terminate the Contract by written notice. If this is done then the Contractor will be paid all amounts to which he is *clause 65* entitled to date and which he has not already been paid and for all all work done prior to the date of determination which is valued at the rates and prices already provided in the Contract.

In addition to this he will be paid amounts in respect of any Preliminary Bill for such items or services contained therein either wholly or in part as certified by the Engineer. He will also recover the costs of materials or goods which he has ordered as being necessary for the Works, including his own plant and Temporary Works, and which should have been delivered or for which he has a legal liability to accept delivery but such materials or goods will become the property of the Employer once he has made appropriate payments to the Contractor.

The Contractor will also be paid an amount equivalent to that which he would reasonably have incurred in expectation of completing the entire Works provided that such an amount is not covered by other forms of payment – it is debatable if this would include loss of profit, but it could include some Head Office overheads and the like.

Insofar as the Contractor's Constructional Plant is concerned the Contractor will be paid the cost of removal from the site to the country of registration of the Contractor or to another destination provided always the cost is no greater – this will also apply to the Plant of the Contractor's Sub-Contractors, both his own and Nominated, and in the case of the latter, the Engineer would determine the costs involved himself and certify accordingly.

The Contractor would also receive payment for all reasonable costs of repatriating the Contractor's staff and workmen employed on or in connection with the Works at the time of temination and this would by implication include any staff and control offices of the Contractor which were not on site but established elsewhere in the country within which the Work was located.

Finally, against all of these payments due to the Contractor, the Employer is entitled to set off any sums due to him by the Contractor in respect of advances for Constructional Plant and materials and for any other monies which were likewise recoverable from the Contractor under the terms of the Contract at the time when the termination occurred.

ucessful ten-
derer

In due course the Employer will consider the advice of the Engineer in the selection of the successful bidder but it is a matter of good business practice that the Employer will advise all people submitting a Tender to him that he does not bind himself to award the Contract to the lowest, or indeed any Tenderer – and this might appear unfair in that Tendering is an extremely expensive business for any Contractor.

It should however be remembered that, should a Contractor have made an error in his Tender which places him in a most unrealistic position in relation to other Tenderers, then the Employer is not bound to accept it if he considers it potentially onerous in the long term to do so – and this clause prevents him from being obliged to do so. Paragraph six of the Proposed Form of Tender releases the Employer from this obligation to accept the lowest or any tender.

mployer –
ariations

Once having entered into a Contract with a Contractor to undertake the works required, the Employer cannot thereafter change or vary the works himself without going through the formalities of requiring the Engineer to issue the necessary Instructions under the appropriate Clauses of the Conditions of the *clause 51* Contract. If the Employer requires the Contractor to vary or change the works as envisaged, or to enter into additional work to suit his requirements, then unless this is done through the Engineer, the Contractor is at liberty to refuse to undertake the variations, changes or additional works but could undertake them at new rates which need have no relationship to those given in the existing Contract.

In these circumstances the Contractor can seek and should agree with the Employer a separate Contract whereby these new works can be undertaken and, in the event of this happening, these new works will not become part of the existing Contract but will have a separate identity. If more suitable to both the Employer and the Contractor the value of these new works could be added to the Contract Price provided it is by mutual agreement and both Parties agree to alter the original Contract.

mpletion of
orks – time for

If this situation arises the Contractor must ensure that he is not involved in a prolongation of his original Contract Period and, if this is likely, he must obtain from the Employer (not the Engineer) agreement that the Employer will instruct the Engineer to issue an appropriate extension to the Time for Completion as *clause 44* being a "special circumstance."

mmencement
works

It is of considerable importance to the Employer that the Works should be constructed within the time allowed and also that the Contractor carries out his obligations both expeditiously and efficiently – if this does not happen then the *clause 41* cost to the Employer can be considerably greater than the amount he recovers by way of liquidated damages.

Because of this the contract enforces specific disciplines upon the Contractor which, if not observed, give the Employer the right to enter the Site and expel the Contractor without legally voiding the Contract or releasing the Contractor from any of his obligations or liabilities. This is referred to as forfeiture by the Contractor and permits the Employer to complete the works himself, or if he wishes, to engage another Contractor to do so on his behalf.

efault by con-
actor

These disciplines are identified positively by holding the Contractor responsible for the consequences if he should abandon the Contract without having a reasonable excuse or in not commencing work as he should have done, or suspending the progress of the work beyond the time to resume of which the *clause 63* Engineer had given him notice or failing to remedy defective work or materials condemned by the Engineer after being given notice by the Engineer, or persistently neglecting to carry out his obligations.

Any one of these failures will entitle the Employer to occupy the Site and the Works and complete them himself. If this happens, the Engineer would immediately provide an evaluation of the amount due to the Contractor up to the time of his failure together with the value of any unused or partly used materials, or any Temporary Works performed to date, and certify the value accordingly.

If deciding to undertake the remaining works himself, the Employer is entitled to retain as much of the Constructional Plant, Temporary Works and materials which had been reserved exclusively for the execution of the Works. He can sell these at any time and apply the proceeds towards any damage he may suffer occasioned by the failure of the Contractor.

Should the Employer in fact undertake the construction of the remaining Works he will be entitled to charge the Contractor all reasonable costs incurred in the construction and maintenance, together with any damages for delay in completion, and in fact all other expenses which the Engineer can properly certify together with all other expenses incurred by the Employer – in the end it is likely that all the Contractor is entitled to receive are such sums, if any, as may be certified by the Engineer as being surplus to the needs of the Employer. If it should happen that the Employer does not recover sufficient money by this means to meet his damages then this is a debt due by the Contractor to the Employer and can be recovered as such in law or by calling the Performance Bond.

default by contractor

bankruptcy – contractor

A further concern of the Employer is if the Contractor should become bankrupt or be subject to a receiving order, or have assigned the Works to someone else without the consent of the Employer – if any of these events occur then exactly the same method of satisfaction can be obtained by the Employer. It is necessary to recognise the legal systems of the country involved because it could be challenged in some countries as to whether the Employer has the right to sell the Contractor's Plant etc. and set off the proceeds as a direct course of action in cases of bankruptcy or liquidation – he may be required to give the proceeds of such sales wholly to the liquidator.   *clause 63*

rates of exchange

Money and cash flow are synonymous in contracting and because of the sometimes violent movement between rates of exchange it is necessary for both the Employer and the Contractor to give serious consideration to this matter.   *clause 72*

currencies

It has become prevalent for the Employer to give, as part of his Instructions to the Tenderers, directions about the currencies to be used for the purchase of goods and services and also about the currency in which payment will be made to the Contractor in performing the Works. Sometimes it is left to the discretion of the Contractor to specify the amounts and in which currency he wishes to be paid.   *clauses 60, 72*

Alternatively a Contractor might consider it of sufficient importance for him to nominate the various currencies and the limits of each currency required by him even if not asked so to do at the time of Tender. If it is necessary for this to be done then it must be stated at the time of Tendering because it cannot be introduced readily thereafter when the Tender has been accepted unless by mutual consent between the Employer and the Contractor.

In the event of a dispute or disagreement of any sort which just cannot be resolved between those responsible for the performance of the Works there exists the opportunity of referring such matters to an arbitrator.

arbitration

The Employer has the same right as the Contractor to refer to arbitration any decision made by the Engineer. The Engineer makes certain decisions solely in his capacity as a professional person, using his expertise for the Enterprise – in this capacity the Engineer is neither an agent of the Employer nor an employee of the Employer within the FIDIC Conditions of Contract.   *clause 67*

When any dispute or disagreement between the Engineer and the Contractor is likely to be referred to arbitration the Engineer maintains his position under the Contract with the Contractor up to and until such time as the reference to arbitration has been confirmed. After that time the Engineer is no longer in a position to settle the matter between the Contractor and the Employer and the Employer is the only Party who can settle with the Contractor on an out-of-Court basis.

There must come a moment in time when everyone agrees and accepts that

rtificate –
aintenance

the Contract is complete in all matters other than those of a liability or procedure in the finalising of accounts and other monetary matters. *clauses 61, 62*

Because of this the Employer will await with interest the issue of a Maintenance Certificate signed by the Engineer which confirms to him that the Works have been completed and maintained to the Engineer's satisfaction. Irrespective of any other form of Certificate which the Engineer issues it is only the Maintenance Certificate which constitutes recognition by the Engineer that the Works have been completed and maintained satisfactorily.

The issue of such a Certificate also is intended to fix the moment of time when the Employer's liability ceases in respect of any obligations he might have towards the Contractor under the Contract unless the Contractor shall have made claims in writing before the issue of the Certificate, but it will obviously not affect those matters not yet resolved which occurred prior to the issue of the Maintenance Certificate because the Contract is deemed to remain active between the Parties until they are all resolved.

The importance of the Maintenance Certificate to the Employer and the Contractor alike is that both should be aware of the extent of any claims which the Contractor wishes to make in respect of his work and the issue of the Maintenance Certificate is often regarded as the terminal point of time when further claims cannot be accepted. This is not necessarily correct because of the suggestion in *clause 52* Clause 60 Part II of the Conditions of Contract that a time period should be established following the issue of the Maintenance Certificate within which the Contractor will submit his Final Account and it could follow that new claim situations might arise then which did not exist earlier.

aims

This would mean that the resolving of these claims which were not in existence before the Maintenance Certificate was issued would be given the same consideration as would those claims which were submitted prior to the issue of the Maintenance Certificate and they are not time-barred simply because the Maintenance Certificate has been issued. Claims which should have been made before the issuing of a Maintenance Certificate and were not presented by then will remain time-barred.

3   THE ENGINEER

The Engineer is not a signatory or party to a FIDIC Contract but is named therein and thereby given a number of duties and responsibilities requiring his expertise in technical design and management. He is cited as an Authority and one who gives instructions and directions and who can exercise options or opinions on appropriate occasions. He can vary the method of construction of the Works to achieve completion but under no circumstances is he empowered to alter the Contract made between the Employer and the Contractor. He can only implement it in accordance with the terms which the parties thereto have agreed.   *clause 2*

The appointment of the Engineer for any Enterprise generally requires him to enter into a separate Contract with the Employer such as the British Association of Consulting Engineers Model Forms of Service Agreements, by which the Employer and the Engineer become bound in Contract – the Engineer and the Employer are not bound together by the FIDIC Conditions of Contract as this is a Contract between the Employer and the Contractor for the construction of the Works but, once the Engineer has been appointed it is customary for the Employer to have complete confidence in him to act in accordance with the requirements of both the FIDIC Contract and their personal Contract which binds them together for this Enterprise.

There can be a number of supplementary Conditions imposed upon the Engineer by the Employer whereby he cannot exercise all of his duties without restraint. The Employer may often wish to be a participant in decision-making, particularly in affairs affecting payment, and in the event of the Engineer being required under the terms of his contract with the Employer to obtain specific approval of the Employer for the execution of any part of these duties then such requirements which affect his responsibility under the FIDIC document will be set out in Part II of the Conditions of Contract and so be known to the Contractor at the time of Tender.

Under the FIDIC Conditions of Contract the Engineer is delegated certain duties and responsibilities which include the issuing of instructions, directions, orders and the giving of information necessary for the construction of the Works to proceed. These responsibilities also require him to comment upon the Contractor's proposals for carrying out the work and require him to ensure that the workmanship and materials are in accordance with the specifications. He determines the measurement and value of work performed by the Contractor and Nominated Sub-Contractors and, in his own right, issues a Certificate of Payment to the Employer stating any payment due to them on both an Interim and Final Basis. It is not the Contractor's application for payment which the Employer recognises but only the Certificate of Payment as issued by the Engineer.

clause 56
clause 36

clause 60

In order that the Engineer can carry out his duties it is permissible for him to delegate in writing to the Engineer's Representatives any of the powers and authority vested in him by the Employer. It would be unacceptable for him to delegate all of his powers to an Engineer's Representative because this would effectively remove from the Contract the expertise in technical design and management of the Engineer himself. He is obliged to provide the Contractor and the Employer with a copy of all such written delegations of powers and authorities he gives to his Representatives.

clause 2

It is required by the Conditions of Contract that the Engineer's Representative is responsible to the Engineer only, notwithstanding that he could be an employee of the Employer and not the Engineer. The duties of the Engineer's Representative are to watch and supervise the work and to ensure that the standards of workmanship employed are in accordance with the specifications – he has no authority to relieve the Contractor of any of his duties or obligations under the Contract nor to involve the Employer in any additional payments other than may be contained within his delegated powers and authorities.

It is becoming customary practice that the Engineer will not delegate to the Engineer's Representative any matters dealing with:

Variation Orders
Engineer's Certificates
Fixing of Rates
Expenditure of Provisional Sums
Approval of Nominated Sub-Contractors
Extensions of Time

*gineers –
presentatives*

The Engineer's Representative's duties and authorities are notified to the Contractor in writing and if the Contractor should receive from the Engineer's Representative any instruction outside the authorities given to him then he must refer the matter immediately to the Engineer. Whilst it is the responsibility of the Engineer's Representative to ensure satisfactory workmanship any failure on his part to disapprove any work or materials would not prevent the Engineer thereafter disapproving such work and ordering it to be removed and reconstructed in accordance with the specification at the Contractor's expense.   *clause 2*

If the Contractor is dissatisfied with any decision of the Engineer's Representative he is entitled to refer the matter to the Engineer who will confirm such decision or change it as he thinks fit.

*sign – respon-
bilities*

The Engineer has no responsibility to the Contractor for the design of the Works nor indeed for those Temporary Works which he designs as part of the Contract – his sole responsibility for design is to the Employer and it is the Contractor, in submitting his Tender, who affirms his ability to construct the work in accordance with the designs provided under the Contract.

It is important to understand the extent of the Engineer's responsibility for the design undertaken by him for the Works – in essence the Engineer designs work for the Employer and in so doing gives no guarantee under the FIDIC Conditions of Contract to the Contractor or anybody else that it can be constructed within reasonable limits of time and price or that it can be constructed at all.

*ntractors –
ligations*

The Engineer's design, as presented for pricing, leaves it to the Contractor's judgement as to whether he can undertake the works or not. If the Contractor decides that he can construct the Works and submits a valid Tender then it is his responsibility and obligation to provide the finished product required under the Contract if his Tender is accepted. Having entered into a Contract to construct the Works the Contractor is liable to pay damages if he does not fulfil his obligations, although under the Conditions of Contract he may be released from these obligations if it is found that it becomes either legally or physically impossible so to do.   *clause 8*

*gineer – negli-
nce*

Whilst the Engineer's responsibilities for design do not exist insofar as the FIDIC Conditions of Contract are concerned, he is obviously at risk if his design is negligent to the extent of putting anyone in danger and particularly towards those who rely on his skill as a professional Engineer to provide such technical knowledge and judgements as are necessary for the Works to be completed.

The Engineer's responsibility for design under the FIDIC Contract can be summarised as follows:

To the Contractor – NONE
To the Employer – NONE

However, under the Engineer's Contract with the Employer (not FIDIC) he may be responsible for:

(1) The application of engineering skills and expertise by which the Works may be designed for construction and operation.

(2) The formulation of necessary Contract Documents including Specifications and Drawings.

(3) The supervision of the construction of the Works by the Contractor.

(4) The provision of all necessary further Drawings, Specifications and Instructions during the course of construction.

It cannot be over-emphasised that whilst it is the Engineer who is responsible for the design of the Works there is nothing in the Contract to require either the Engineer or the Employer to guarantee by an expressed or even implied term that such designs are capable of being constructed. It is the contractor who warrants he can execute the design and construct the Works simply by the act of submitting his Tender.

expressed/ implied term

There is sometimes doubt about the distinction between "expressed terms" and "implied terms" and it is simply that the former are those terms which are actually written into the Contract, whereas the latter are terms which are still part of the Contract although they are not written into it – for example, on the Site for a Works occupied only a small portion of land within a much larger area owned by the Employer, then without an expressed term being necessary, it would be an implied term that the Employer would grant right of access to the Site to the Contractor so he could do the work. It is also an implied term that all parties concerned with the Works will perform their responsibilities and duties with reasonable care, skill and diligence.

Recognising the many complications which can arise during the construction of any Works and the daily involvement of people with high technical skills it is necessary for a discipline or procedure to be established as to who is to give orders and who is responsible for carrying them out.

engineer's satis- faction

The FIDIC Conditions of Contract make it clear that it is the Engineer who needs to be satisfied with the proper execution and the maintenance of the Works and it is he who is given authority to issue instructions and directions on any matter concerning the Works whether mentioned in the Contract or not – all such *clause 13* instructions and directions shall be obeyed by the Contractor provided always that it is legally and physically possible to carry them out.

directions and instructions

Certain of the instructions and directions issued by the Engineer or his Representative concern the day-to-day matters of administration or the implementation of the requirements for physical construction of the Works which the Contractor is obliged to observe under the Contract – whereas others constitute a direct Order which could carry possibilities of changes to the Contract Price and extensions to the Time for Completion.

The Employer cannot issue any instruction himself to the Contractor but must always go through the appointed Engineer – in like manner, the Engineer will not instruct any Sub-Contractors directly (unless on matters of urgency) but must do so only through the Contractor.

approval by engineer

An explanation is sometimes sought as to the meaning of "approval by the Engineer" and whether approval can be withheld or can be used to dictate the Engineer's wishes compared with those of the Contractor.

In general terms the position is that the Contractor is solely responsible for the construction and maintenance of the Works and this includes the methods by which the Works are constructed.

However, it may be necessary for the Contractor to receive the approval of the Engineer for certain methods which he would like to use; if the Engineer's approval is not obtained, the Contractor must adopt different methods.

specification

By way of example, if a specification refers to excavation in the most general terms and it does not expressly make reference to it being done either manually or by machine then the Contractor is completely free to choose which method to adopt. However, if the method of excavation needs to receive the Engineer's approval, and the Engineer does not approve of machine excavation, then the excavation done manually by the Contractor will not attract any additional payment should the Contractor have priced excavation work on the assumption that it would be carried out by machine.

If, however, approval by the Engineer was not required, but the Engineer would only accept the excavation being done manually, this would constitute a Variation and the Contractor be paid accordingly.

ommencement

It is the Engineer's responsibility to give a written order for the commencement of the Work, and at the same time pass on to the Contractor the Employer's authority to occupy the Site legally and physically.

clause 41

It is particularly of importance to ensure that the Engineer's order to commence is given in writing as required – without it there can be no official commencement of the Works within the meaning of the Contract and this would mean that the Time for Completion would have no specific starting point from which to run and in consequence there could be no effective date for Completion of the Works. This could prevent the Employer securing liquidated damages should the time taken by the Contractor to perform the work exceed the time which would otherwise have been reasonable had a written order been properly given.

Having once given the written order to commence however the Engineer must make certain that the Contractor does in fact start work properly within the specified period given in the Appendix to the Conditions of Contract and also to record that the Time for Completion is determined from the last day of the commencement period and extends from that time by the number of days within which the Contractor has undertaken to complete the Works.

ariations

For anything to be subjected to a Variation there must obviously be a basis from which a Variation can arise and, in the context of civil engineering construction, it is generally referred to within the document as being the "Scope of the Work" – this would describe the nature of the Works, be it the construction of a highway, airfield, dam or any other utility and would give an immediate identification of the type of work to be undertaken and generally give a sufficiently detailed description for the Contractor to understand its extent.

clause 51

ope of works

The Scope of the Works, once having been defined, will attract numerous alterations or changes in order to adapt successfully to circumstances which could not necessarily have been foreseen when the Works were first envisaged – such changes might be requested by the Contractor to suit his construction methods or by the Engineer when producing the working drawings. Sometimes the Employer initiates changes to suit his financial or commercial circumstances or to take advantage of technical improvements or innovations.

Because of the inevitable need to make changes to the original concept a Clause is included within the Conditions whereby Variations can be made and which defines the procedures and requirements whereby such Variations might be processed. Only the Engineer has the authority to vary the Works by giving an order to the Contractor – he is permitted to make changes of almost any kind but generally with the implied purpose of achieving final completion of the Works.

riations

It is obviously necessary to consider that Variations as such must have some restriction to remain within the intentions of the Parties when entering into Contract although individual Employers and indeed many Engineers see the need for Variations to range from being of little consequence to ones of considerable magnitude.

clause 51

It would generally be accepted that all Variations which are necessary or desirable are made by the Engineer simply to achieve the completion of the Works as envisaged within the Scope of the Works and no more, and certainly should not commit the Contractor to duplicate the Works or to introduce works alien to the original concept and to result in a final financial involvement out of all proportion to the original Contract Price.

riations –
itten/verbal

Whilst there might be a difference of opinion as to whether certain work constitutes Variation within the meaning as defined or whether it is really already part of the work to be undertaken by the Contractor, it is stated that the Contractor will not commence any Variation until he has received an Order in writing from the Engineer. However, the Engineer, if he considers it desirable, can give

the order verbally and the Contractor is still obliged to comply with this whether   *clause 51*
or not he gets it confirmed in writing before obeying the order.

    If the Engineer gives an order verbally and does not follow it up in writing
then providing the Contractor writes to the Engineer within seven days confirm-
ing the instruction he has been given and receives no reply from the Engineer
during the following fourteen days then it shall be deemed that the Order from
the Engineer had been made in writing.

    In the context of the Engineer being empowered by the Employer to give
instructions to the Contractor it is essential to the well-being of the Enterprise as a
whole that the Engineer gives his instructions clearly, promptly and precisely and
that he has studied and understood the financial and Time for Completion consequences of his instructions beforehand. Equally the Engineer should be aware of

approval   the consequences of giving approval of Works at times too far removed from the
time the Works were executed. It is incumbent on the Engineer to be aware of the   *clause 13*
need to give approval or otherwise of the Works as soon as they have been executed and to be aware of the advantages to the Employer of the timely issue of
instructions so that the Contractor can plan and execute variations to the Works
economically and expeditiously. At the same time the Engineer should be prepared to advise his Employer that any variations required by the Employer might
have very serious consequences in respect of the capital costs of the Works and the
Time for Completion.

    It should not be forgotten that Clause 41 places upon the Contractor the re-
sponsibility and duty to proceed with due expedition and without delay unless
otherwise sanctioned or ordered by the Engineer – therefore if the Engineer fails
to perform any of his required duties or obligations on time or within a reasonable

work – contrac-   time and this should result in the Contractor failing to fulfil his particular obli-
tor to proceed   gation of expedition then the Contractor might be entitled to recover any ad-   *clause 41*
expeditiously   ditional costs incurred together with an appropriate extension to the Time for
Completion.

    The question is sometimes posed as to the status to be given to a Drawing
issued by the Engineer to the Contractor and whether it might constitute a
written Variation Order – obviously, the content of the Drawing will be the pre-
determining factor in that some Drawings merely amplify or give particular

drawings –   instructions to the Contractor concerning work already covered by the Specifi-
status   cation and obviously these could not be regarded as an ordinary Variation.   *clause 6*
However, when a Drawing is issued which shows a change in the Works as orig-
inally contemplated and such a change can be identified as a Variation, then the
Drawing itself will be accepted as being a written Order from the Engineer to the
Contractor within the meaning of the Clause. In such a case the Contractor must
fulfil its requirements in exactly the same way as if he had received a communication in the form of a letter or notice.

    The granting to the Engineer of the powers to vary the Works is essential, in
that a Contract without such a clause would not permit changes of any sort to be
made to the physical construction of the Works. This would result in each and

variations   every change which was desired necessitating a separate Contract being made   *clause 51*
between the Employer and the Contractor and for them to agree specific rates for
the work and to consider the effect which such work has upon the Contract
already in operation.

    An Order in writing from the Engineer is not required for any changes in
quantity for any work which is seen to be merely the result of the quantities being
different from those stated in the Bill of Quantities. It is known that the quantities
which are provided are estimated quantities only for the Works and are not to be
taken as the actual or correct quantities to be executed by the Contractor. This   *clause 51*
therefore permits such changes in quantities to become contractually acceptable
without any need for the Contractor to seek a Variation Order.

    Having issued a Variation Order the Engineer must take into consideration
how it affects payment to the Contractor and, provided the work involved is the

variations –   same in character and within such timing as that work already described in the   *clause 52*
payment   Bill of Quantities, then existing rates for such work shall be applicable.

If the Contract does not contain any rates or prices applicable to the varied work then suitable rates or prices should be agreed between the Engineer and the Contractor. If they are unable to agree on suitable rates then the Engineer's decision as to what are reasonable and proper rates will prevail. There are Contracts which appear to have suitable rates for varied work already within the Bills of Quantities but it must be recognised that such rates in the Bill of Quantities are related to a time-based programme of execution. If it happens that the work is done out of the time sequence on which the rates were based then the rates themselves are not applicable and must be subject to change and be made reasonable and proper under the prevailing circumstances.

Variations – new rates

clause 52

A situation will arise where certain changes affecting a particular trade can directly or indirectly influence the reasonableness of prices contained for other work not directly associated with it and, if by reason of a Variation Order issued by the Engineer, any of the other rates in the Bill of Quantities are rendered unreasonable or inapplicable, then a suitable rate or price shall be agreed by the Engineer and the Contractor.

By way of example, if due to Variation Orders affecting the foundations of a bridge the construction of the superstructure was delayed for a considerable period, then this clause would enable the Contractor to seek a change in the rates for ancillary work such as balustrading, kerbing, lighting and surfacing because of increased costs arising from inflation during the delay period, from out-of-sequence working and possible changes in the method of executing the work which would make the original Contract rates unreasonable or unrealistic. Under such circumstances the Contractor is entitled to have them altered to a suitable price or rate as may be agreed between the Engineer and himself – even though not a direct part of the Variation Order itself.

Variations – example of rate change

clause 52

If it is intended by the Engineer to vary a rate or price already in the Bill of Quantities because of the direct effect of the issue of a Variation Order, or the indirect effect that such a Variation Order might have on other items of work, then it is incumbent upon the Engineer to give notice to the Contractor in writing either before the commencement of such work, or as soon thereafter as is practicable of his intention to vary a rate or price. If this is not done the rate remains unchanged.

Variations – notice of change of rate

Likewise in the same manner, the Contractor is obliged to give notice in writing to the Engineer of his intention to claim any extra payment on a varied rate or price arising from any increase or decrease because a Variation Order has been issued.

It is regretted that for the establishment of suitable or new rates or prices no specified time limit is given within which this is to be done – however, it can be argued that, as the Engineer has the responsibility for measuring and valuing the work fully and properly at regular intervals in accordance with the Conditions of Contract Part II, he would be obliged to have established the new rates during the same interval so as to have completely fulfilled his obligations to value the work correctly.

Again by way of example, in the fixing of new rates, should the Bill of Quantities contain an item of concrete relating to only a single and specified strength or mix and a Variation Order is issued requiring concrete of a different strength or mix it will be necessary to establish a completely new rate from first principles and not to rely upon a hypothetical analysis of a rate for concrete which is already available. There is no obligation upon the Contractor to provide a build-up of any rate already in the Bill of Quantities but, from time to time, it may be tactically prudent to give a breakdown of a rate.

Variations – example of fixing new rate

clause 52

The reason for this logic concerning the formulation of a new rate is that, when pricing the Bill of Quantities, the Contractor is entitled to disperse his overheads and profit margin in any way or manner he thinks fit. Because of this, a situation could arise where certain rates appear unreasonable and possibly unrealistic and therefore to use them for Varied Work, which was never part of his original Tender, would be incorrect.

It would follow that in the absence of any obligation requiring new rates to be related to those already existing in the Bill of Quantities, the Engineer must determine what is a suitable rate in all the prevailing circumstances and ignore the availability of any rates for work even of a similar nature already in the Bill of Quantities. If, however, the conditions require new rates to be analogous to existing rates, then the position becomes totally different and the Contractor's build-up of the original rates becomes important.

preliminary bill

The Engineer would also have to include the direct or indirect effect upon items contained in a Preliminary Bill (if one exists) and to ensure that when valuing any Variation Order he would include the financial effects on such items in the Preliminary Bill not only in respect of any direct cost influence but also of the effect of any time factor involved.

The Engineer can only issue a Variation Order in so far as he has authority so to do, and, if he acts outside this authority, the Employer can refuse to make payment to the Contractor and leave it to the Contractor to seek satisfaction from the Engineer outside the Contract.

variation – omission

The Engineer may issue a Variation Order to omit work but not just to have it done by another Contractor – neither is the Engineer permitted to give any Variation Orders during the Maintenance Period, although he is entitled to require the Contractor to execute any remedial or maintenance work (generally excluding fair wear and tear) during this period because until all work has been completed the Contractor remains responsible for total fulfilment of his obligations and only when this has been done will the Engineer issue a Maintenance Certificate.

waiver

The Engineer need not issue a Variation Order in respect of a concession or of a waiver made by him in respect of specifications, standards, or any changed manner of construction which the Contractor may have requested but can do so if he wishes as being an option which only he can exercise and this would be in the form of an Order on technical or specification matters but at no cost to the Employer.

If the Contractor varies the work without authority, he is not entitled to be paid for the work he has done in lieu and it is arguable whether he should be paid for the work he should have done anyway. He will in fact have breached the Contract even if the work he has done is better than that originally required. The Engineer can accept any improved standard of work but need pay only at the unit rates and prices in the Bill of Quantities.

variations – contractor extra work responsibility

It is sometimes argued that the Contractor only commits himself to performing the Works as indicated at the time of Tender and that any Variation Orders issued by the Engineer do not oblige him to carry the same responsibility or liability as for the works he originally undertook. This is not so because the Contractor *clause 51* has already undertaken to execute all the Engineer's instructions on any matter, whether mentioned in the Contract or not, and in so doing he will have given an implied undertaking that such instructions and directions as issued by the Engineer will also be executed under exactly the same Conditions as the original Works and would likewise carry the same responsibilities as for the original Work.

Finally, the Engineer has no power to vary the rate or price of any item when no Variation Order has been made or where the actual quantities are more or less than those shown in the Bill of Quantities – it is only when a Variation Order has been issued that any change in rates or prices can be contemplated.

completion – extension due to variations

The Variation Orders issued by the Engineer may affect the Time for Completion but only the Engineer can determine the amount of any extension due to *clauses 43, 44,* the Contractor and advise him accordingly.   *51*

Additional Work, and indeed indirect and external influences such as strikes and material shortages, can extend the time required to complete the works to beyond the period allowed. Certain, but not all causes will permit the contract period to be extended and so enable the Contractor to avoid paying liquidated damages but the fact that an extension of time is granted does not necessarily mean the Contractor will obtain extra payment for this happening.

completion of works – extension

Whilst it is the responsibility of the Engineer to determine the amount of an extension and to notify the Employer and the Contractor accordingly it is of far greater importance to the Contractor to make the necessary submission to the Engineer in good time giving the details and circumstances which have arisen and which, in his view, justify an extension to the Time of Completion being granted.

clauses 43, 44

The Engineer is not bound to take into account, but obviously could do so if he wished as this is optional, any circumstances which the Contractor considers will justify an extension of time even when the Contractor has failed to submit full and detailed particulars of such a claim within the twenty-eight days required after the work has commenced, or as soon thereafter as was practicable.

During the period of construction various changes in both work and value can be very significant indeed and an adjusted Contract Price based on the straightforward application of unit rates to value variations might be unfair to Employer and Contractor alike.

variations exceeding 10%

Because of this and upon the completion of the entire Works and in making a study of the draft Final Account should it be found that there is a reduction or increase greater than 10% of the sum named by the Employer in the Letter of Acceptance (excluding all fixed sums, provisional sums and dayworks), and this reduction or increase resulted from the aggregate effect of all the Variation Orders and the adjustment of actual against estimated quantities (but excluding all provisional sums, dayworks and adjustments to the Contract Price for Variations in Labour/Materials or changes in national or state legislation affecting the basic structure of each unit rate) then the Contract Price shall be adjusted.

clause 52

This adjustment will be by such sums as may be agreed between the Engineer and the Contractor both having regard to all relevant factors which would include, amongst other matters, the Contractor's site and general overhead costs incurred in the execution of the Works.

Cash flow depends firstly upon the Contractor making an Application to be paid – secondly by the Engineer advising the Employer the amount to be paid – and thirdly by the Employer paying the Contractor within the period as stipulated in the contract.

certificate – payment

The Engineer is obliged to issue Certificates of Payment within the times required by the Contract and is not permitted to withhold any Certificate unless it is expressly stated in the Contract.

clause 60

The documents will make clear which items he is to value and will also give direction about the amount of percentage of Retention Money to be applied to the Contract as a whole, or where given in sections, to the individual amount for each section.

There will also be stated in the Appendix A a minimum amount below which an Interim Certificate will not be issued – such an amount would include all Sub-Contractor's payments due and all other matters which ultimately affect the Contract Price in addition to the Contractor's own work.

Because it is of greater importance for the Contractor to study his rights concerning payments than it is for the Engineer to certify, this subject has been given in greater detail in the chapter concerning the Contractor.

The interest of the employer in the Maintenance Certificate has been mentioned previously but it is the Engineer who makes the important decision when issuing such a Certificate covering the acceptability of the work performed by the Contractor.

certificate – maintenance

The Engineer is aware of the fact that when the Maintenance Certificate is issued by him it advises the Employer that the Engineer is satisfied with the performance of all the Contractor's work – he is also aware that he must not accept any unregistered claims which the Contractor could, but had not, submitted earlier.

clauses 61, 62

He will also recognise that because the Contractor is given a time period following the issue of the Maintenance Certificate within which to submit his version of the Final Account new claims can arise during such period which have not, or could not, have appeared previously – these new claims can emerge whilst assessing the value of the work performed for inclusion in the Final Account.

final account

Under these circumstances the Engineer should accept the presentation of these further claims in the same manner as he has accepted all others. These are not time-barred simply by the issue of the Maintenance Certificate because of the proviso that the Employer shall remain liable for the fulfilment of all his obligations notwithstanding the issue of a Maintenance Certificate, and one of these *clause 52* obligations is the payment of the Engineer's Final Certificate of Payment. The Maintenance Certificate is the penultimate Certificate issued by the Engineer and his Final Certificate for Payment of the Final Account remains until the last. *clause 62*

claims

4 THE CONTRACTOR

Probably two of the best known Enterprises which have survived both time and weather are the Pyramids at Giza in Egypt which were constructed for Pharaoh Cheops approximately forty-five centuries ago, and more recently the Taj Mahal at Agra in India, some three centuries ago, for Emperor Shah Jahan.

Whilst the Employers are known by name, possibly only historians could recall the names of the "Engineers" involved but, in both instances, it is said that their particular place in history arose from their early demise at the hands of their Employers – not through a fault in the design of their work – but simply because the Employers were ensuring that their "Engineers" could not embark upon further Enterprises of the same nature which would rival their own.

These Enterprises had two features in common in that they were both constructed by direct labour and in each case no mention is found in recorded history of any reference to a Contractor being involved.

The emergence of the Contractor into the construction business began two or three centuries ago by some individual enterprising craftsman recognising that, by combining his skills with other craftsmen, he could be in a position to undertake complete works and not rely solely upon work of his own particular trade. This has now resulted in the formation of a large industry which concentrates its efforts on undertaking construction work of various types.

A large Enterprise can be undertaken by a single company or, where more suitable, by a Joint Venture, a legal joining together of two or more companies for the purpose of constructing the Works. The companies in the Joint Venture are *Joint ventures* jointly and severally bound to execute the Works and in the event of one going into liquidation, then the other party or parties to the Joint Venture are obliged to continue the work unless they all, in turn, enter into liquidation.

Where the Works are of a particularly large, or of a more specialised nature, a Consortium of Contractors, each a specialist in his own particular field of work, is formed – for example, a new steel works might require a separate Contractor for the Civil Work, Blast Furnaces, Coke Ovens, Services, Railways and ancillary *Consortium* undertakings, all Contractors again being bound as a single entity and carrying a continuing responsibility for completion should any member enter into liquidation, but each providing his own expertise of a specialist nature and accepting direct responsibility for the part of the Works appropriate to his skills.

With Joint Ventures or Consortia it is imperative that all Parties involved in them have complete faith in each other and that one company only is appointed as leader or sponsor – preferably the strongest and most able company. It is equally important that the Contractor's project manager on site should be a member of the sponsor company.

Insofar as the nature of any Works are concerned and irrespective of the legal formations of these companies, as and when they enter into Contract with an Employer, they become known simply as the "Contractor".

No matter by which manner the Contractor has become involved in being *Tender* invited to submit a Tender he will immediately recognise that once he undertakes the preparation of the Tender he will incur expense, often of considerable magnitude.

He knows this particular expense is not recoverable directly from the Employer (as he is not in Contract to produce a Tender but is doing so because of his own wishes) and is aware that most Employers invite Tenders with the qualification that they are not obliged to accept the lowest one they receive or pay for its preparation if not accepted.

However, having made the decision to Tender and having embarked upon its preparation there are many factors which the Contractor must recognise and deal with and, whilst these might be of varying importance or be given different priorities by individual Contractors, there is certainly the need for each of these matters to be considered fully. It should not be forgotten that failure to give full consideration to all the contents of the Tender Documents and naively believing that everything will be all right in the end is the surest way of putting at risk the future of any construction company.

tender – considerations

The many stages of activities which occur during the life of a Contract can be divided conveniently so that they may be considered at the appropriate times:

1. Pre-Tender;
2. Construction/Maintenance;
3. Completion.

The commentary which is given below on each stage is a sequence which might be followed by a Contractor who successfully tenders for, obtains and completes the Civil Engineering Work of the Enterprise.

Many of the comments in this Pre-Tender stage are equally valid for the Construction stage but they are made in the Pre-Tender stage because such matters need to be considered carefully whilst the Contractor is preparing his Tender. Nevertheless the reader should carry forward in his mind most, if not all of this Pre-Tender stage, when studying the Construction stage. The comments have not been re-written to avoid unnecessary repetition.

1. PRE-TENDER

During the Pre-Tender period the Contractor will expend a considerable amount of energy and money in the preparation of his Tender, and often he will feel that the time allowed is extremely short to accomplish all that he is required to do.

Ideally he should receive a number of documents including drawings, which should demonstrate that the Works have reached an advanced state of design leaving very little to be settled when the Works on Site begin but regrettably this does not always happen.

geological report

If the actual Report on Geological Information is not issued as a Tender Document it should always be made available for inspection at the Engineer's office and it is necessary for the Contractor to examine it in detail because if he prepares a Tender which does not properly take into account all the information *clause 11* which was available, even if not necessarily issued, then he will suffer the consequences.

site visit

There are a number of matters concerning his Tender which can be done within the confines of his own office but the Contractor must give serious thought *clause 11* to visiting the Site and particularly becoming acquainted with, and aware of, local conditions and significant relevant factors within the country concerned.

Following any visit to Site there will be further deliberations to formulate, analyse and finally present the Tender. Various subject-matters with a guide to their involvement in the preparation of any Tender follow in a reasonable chronological order.

Instructions to Tenderers – whilst these are generally, but not always, provided within the Tender Documents, the Contractor should ensure that they become part of the Contract Documents as and when he signs his Tender and Form of Agreement. The Instructions to Tenderers are given to all tendering Contractors and are intended to set out in detail the many items which the Engineer considers to be of importance and whereby he is able to give direction about important matters of a contractual nature or technical specification which may not be found elsewhere in the Documents.

For those not familiar with Instructions to Tenderers the following broad outline is typical but not exhaustive of information given – obviously different types of Work, and indeed different Employers and Engineers, will require a varying degree of emphasis being placed on different aspects of the Instructions. The reader is provided with guidance on what might be expected with comments as appropriate in the ensuing paragraphs.

Tender Documents – The Instructions to Tenderers will list the Documents which comprise the Tender and it should not be forgotten that in arguments which develop during the Contract, or indeed afterwards in Arbitration, only these Documents which are listed can be referred to in such disputes unless a special circumstance arises where reference to other documents obviously is necessary.

(1) Instruction to Tenderers
(2) Form of Tender (with Appendix)
(3) Conditions of Contract
(4) Specifications
(5) Drawings
(6) Bill of Quantities
(7) Circular letters from the Engineer
(8) Geological data.

All of these should form an integral part of the Contract and are referred to in detail where appropriate.

Scope of Works – within the Documents there should be a description of the type, nature and extent of the Works which is generally referred to as the Scope of the Works. This gives the Contractor a reasonable indication of the work to be done when pricing the Tender.

The Scope of the Works does not necessarily set any limits as to the extent of the Works to be undertaken, but to go beyond the description and introduce work of a different character after the Contract has been signed would not be acceptable unless by agreement between the Parties to the Contract.

It sometimes happens for motorways to be increased in length, airfields to be enlarged and ancillary work to be increased with no complaint being made by the Parties but if, for example, the Contractor was instructed to erect a building or dwelling within a motorway contract by Variation Order then he could refuse to accept such an instruction.

It would, however, be quite acceptable to extend the Scope of the Works to include additional works of the same character as there is no defined limitation of money value beyond which the extent of the Scope of the Works cannot be increased above the Contract Price – although the Contract Price will be adjusted if the value of the additional works exceeds or is less than 10% of the sum named in the Letter of Acceptance.

Obviously, to attempt to double the Scope of the Works or significantly increase it would give the Contractor grounds for complaint if it suited him, but providing the additional work in value is realistic in relation to the work originally intended then no complaint would be justified.

For example – the Works are intended to comprise a twenty-kilometre length of six-lane dual-carriage motorway together with three underpasses and eighteen bridges – plus certain other ancillary works. Although the Scope of the Works gives a definite length of motorway it affords no opportunity to the Contractor to claim that once he has completed the twenty kilometres then, at least so far as he is concerned, the Contract is completed, and thereafter to argue that the Engineer's Instruction by way of a Variation Order to execute a further three kilometres or construct a further two bridges is invalid. This is not so because the Contractor will have undertaken when he signed the Contract to carry out Varied and Additional Works on the instruction of the Engineer and no limit is placed on bona fide additional works which might be ordered.

The importance of the Scope of the Works is that it gives the Contractor an indication of his obligations and in particular gives him a clear understanding

Instructions to Tenderers

Tender Documents

clause 11

Scope of works

Variation – Exceeding 10%

clause 52

about the nature and technical requirements of the Works.

Visiting Site and Examining Documents – whereas the Conditions of Contract state that the Contractor shall be deemed to have inspected the Site the Instructions to Tenderers might alter that to "shall visit the Site" and make a Site visit obligatory. The Contractor must be reminded also to satisfy himself completely about the risks, obligations and responsibilities the Employer wishes him to undertake. Generally he will be told that all costs and charges in connection *clause 11* with a visit to and examination of the Site must be borne by the Tenderer as indeed must all other costs involved in preparing the Tender.

Indemnity to the Employer – The Instructions will also state that any persons or companies involved in the preparation of the Tender, or their servants or agents, who might be granted permission by the Employer to enter the Site for the purpose of a pre-tender inspection must indemnify the Employer completely against all conceivable forms of personal loss or damage which might arise. Note should be taken of the need to be "granted permission" – this being a formal requirement as without it the Contractor is not allowed to enter the Site – the fact that he is bidding for the work does not in itself assume permission has been granted.

Programme – The Contractor should expect to be told precisely when the Employer wishes the work to commence and at the same time give the number of days allowed for completion. In some cases the Contractor may be asked to give a *clause 14* starting time and his time for completion and this information could influence the selection of the successful bidder.

Tender Documents to be completed – The Tenderer must bid for the execution of the whole of the Works and not just parts to suit his own particular purposes. The Tender Letter must be signed by a person authorised to do so on *tender letter* behalf of the Tenderer. For the purposes of serving notices the Tenderer must *business address* state the principal place of business or such other address. *clause 68*

Submission of Tender – The Instructions to Tenderers will state the manner *tender – submission* in which the Tender will be submitted. Sometimes the Tenders will be opened in public and in the presence of representatives of the other Tendering Contractors – this practice is one which is not favoured so much today as it was in the past because of the many qualifications which are now received with Tenders. Until these qualifications have been quantified it is not possible at the public opening to readily identify the lowest Tender.

The Tenderers will be instructed also about the manner of presentation of *tender – presentation* their Tenders; this is generally for the documents to be contained in a sealed envelope addressed to the Engineer and the envelope should have no words or marks on it which might identify the name of the Tendering Contractor. Often a second envelope is required in which is enclosed priced Bills of Quantities, separate from the other documents, generally to be opened only if a particular Tender is being considered seriously.

Information will also be given about the latest date and time (local time) *tender – time/date* when the Tenders must be received and about the procedure to be adopted if the Contractor wishes to withdraw his Tender before it has been opened. If delivery by post is specified then this method must be adopted, otherwise a bid may be disqualified.

No alteration to be made to the Documents – The Tendering Contractor will be told that no alteration can be made to the Tender Form or any of the Tender Documents attached thereto and if any alteration is made then the Tender may *tender – alterations* be rejected – and also that no Tender will be considered if it is incomplete or improperly filled in. Incomplete in this instance would not mean the omission of some unit rates in the Bills of Quantities. Each item in the Bill is expected to be priced, or if it is left unpriced, it will be deemed to be that the cost of the work *tender – incomplete* described in the item has been allowed for elsewhere in the Tender.

Pricing – All items in the Bills of Quantities in the Document are priced for the Tender and extended in ink or indelible marking. Any alteration or change to the figures must be initialled by the person signing the Form of Tender. The rates and prices set down by the Tenderer against the items in the Bills of Quantities *ender – pricing* are to be the full inclusive value of the finished work as described and are to include for profit. All obligations and liabilities of any sort whatsoever (except where specifically stated to the contrary elsewhere in the Documents) are to be borne by the Contractor and the costs thereof included in the rates and prices.

ender – period available Further information – During the Tendering Period, the Engineer may issue further information, clarifications or corrections to the Contract Documents, all of which will be given in the form of a notice from the Engineer which will become part of the Tender and be signed by the Tenderer to indicate that all such confirmation, corrections etc., have been taken into consideration when establishing the rates and prices.

ender – queries Following a study of the Contract Documents and a visit to Site, the Contractor might have a number of queries as to the interpretation of the Documents which comprise the Tender and these he should present to the Engineer in writing. In replying to the Contractor, the Engineer should also communicate the query and his answer to all other Tendering Contractors and if of sufficient importance to affect the Tender, the correspondence will be included within the Contract Documents and become part thereof.

ender – lowest Acceptance – As a matter of formality the Employer will generally state that he does not bind himself to accept the lowest or any Tender and will not give a reason for the acceptance of the Tender other than the lowest and will not give reasons why he has rejected any Tender.

ender – time available Time Available for Tender – It is important to the Contractor at a very early stage of Tendering to make certain that sufficient time is given him to provide a bona fide and viable Tender. If he decides that there is insufficient time then he should communicate immediately with the Engineer and ask for an extension of time. It is no good attempting to produce a Tender if the time available does not permit it to be done properly and with great thoroughness – errors or misjudgements which occur during this time can never be corrected once the Contract has been signed and any sympathy extended towards the Contractor inevitably falls short of extra payment.

egally/ physically impossible Legally and Physically Impossible – Before proceeding in detail with the preparation of the Tender the Contractor should be aware of the legality and physical possibility of performing the Works forming the Enterprise. If events subsequently prove that it was physically impossible at the time he tendered he is then responsible to the Employer and will pay damages arising from his failure to fulfil his liabilities to complete the work he undertook to do for the Employer.   *clause 13*

rustration At the time of submitting a Tender it is the Contractor who warrants that the Works are physically possible to construct but if events occurring after the Contract make it physically impossible to continue then the Contract becomes frustrated and the Contractor is paid exactly in the same manner as if a war had intervened and the Contract terminated.   *clauses 65, 66*

If after commencing the Contract the Contractor is instructed to execute additional work which is physically impossible then the Engineer's instruction and directions in this matter are invalid but if such instructions are believed by the Engineer to be physically possible and technically sound but the Contractor takes a view to the contrary a situation arises which requires particular understanding by both Parties in order to find a solution.   *clause 13*

By way of example, if the Engineer instructs the Contractor, who is also a specialist in piling work, to undertake additional work by providing more piles of given length and diameter to sustain a given load, then, if the Contractor in his experience considers that this is impracticable or if done as such presents a risk of collapse of the superstructure, then he is obliged, for his own protection, to make these matters known to the Engineer.

If the Engineer insists that the additional work is carried out strictly in accordance with his instructions, then the Contractor should seek a second authoritative opinion. If this opinion confirms the Contractor's own view, and yet fails to persuade the Engineer to change his instructions the Contractor should advise both the Engineer and the Employer that he is not accepting this instruction because it conflicts with his legal and moral obligations to safeguard both the

Employer and the public at large. If this fails he should give notice of his complaint as a dispute under the Contract and seek an immediate Arbitration.

Insofar as the legality of an Enterprise is concerned if constructing a gaming house, or erecting a private distillery for alcohol in a country which regards these Enterprises as illegal, then in the event of having entered into a Contract to construct such Enterprises, both the Employer and Contractor have acted contrary to the Law and, therefore, no legal Contract exists and neither is in a position to present a legal action against the other.

Liquidated Damages – It is possibly one of the most distressing outcomes of any Contract for a Contractor to fail to perform the work within the allowed Time for Completion and to find that he becomes liable to pay Liquidated Damages – often considerably in excess of any profit which he has earned. In such a situation a Contractor might become bankrupt and it is therefore important at the Tender stage that he makes a very shrewd judgement as to whether the consequences of failure to perform will not destroy him. *clause 47*

The amount of Liquidated Damages is intended to be a pre-assessment by the Employer of the damage he will suffer, on either a daily or weekly basis, should the Works not be completed and he is not able to take possession of them at the appropriate time. The amount of Liquidated Damages can vary considerably in value according to circumstances. If the amount of Liquidated Damages is assessed at too low a level a Contractor might be tempted to add to his Tender Sum the cost of some additional months of contract time to cover the amount of damages – in such a case the payment of such damages would be less than the allowance for the costs of the over-run and the costs to accelerate to complete the Works within the Time for Completion required by the Tender Documents.

On the other hand Liquidated Damages can appear very excessive in relation to the Contract Value and, by way of an example, a Contract for the construction of an off-loading facility for goods from ships could have Liquidated Damages disproportionately high when compared to the Contract Value if the Employer has to contend with a number of cargo boats resting idle in the river estuary unable to off-load and with mounting sums for demurrage charges and other costs continuing until the Works have been completed.

Liquidated Damages are intended to be a commercially calculated figure which bears a relationship to the realities of the costs expected to be incurred by the Employer if unable to occupy the Works on time and in no way should be regarded as a penalty upon the Contractor.

The commitment to pay Liquidated Damages to the Employer is one which the Contractor enters into when Tendering but if he could subsequently demonstrate that they were unreasonable or unrealistic in the context of the real damage suffered by the Employer then the local courts might be expected to adjust the amount to a more realistic value notwithstanding the Contractor having already committed himself to pay a higher figure under the Contract.

The Contract provides for a reduction of the total amount of Liquidated Damages for delay when any part or section of the Works has been certified by the Engineer as complete and where such part or sections of the Works have been occupied or used by the Employer before the whole of the Works as such has been completed.

Contractor's Construction Capacity – It is obviously of considerable importance to the Contractor that he does not extend himself beyond any limits of performance of which he is capable and in this matter he must realise that in tendering for the Works he invites acceptance of his offer and, if it is accepted, it is no good then complaining that it is really beyond his capacity to undertake or that there are certain intervening reasons such as other work which he has accepted, which preclude him from doing the Works under offer. *clause 8*

Once he has offered to do the Works and the offer has been accepted then he is obliged to complete the Works.

Having been satisfied that the Scope of the Works is within his technical ability he must also satisfy himself that the execution of the Works is feasible insofar as his available managerial, plant and labour resources exist and that he is not subjecting himself to undue risk by undertaking such a programme of work – he would need to consider the costs of additional staff, labour, etc., necessary for the Works and, because it is his obligation to provide all labour, plant etc., he has no claim upon the Employer should this prove difficult or seemingly become impossible to satisfy.

contractors – finance and cash flow

Contractor's Financial Capacity – In this present day of high interest rates it is essential for the Tendering Contractor to consider his forecast cash flow and relate his anticipated expenditure to his potential earnings and then determine whether or not he has the financial capacity to cover any negative difference which might exist. Most probably he will obtain the necessary facilities from his own Bank or a Bank in the country where the Works are located if transfer of funds are restricted by currency controls.

employer – funding

However, the present-day method of tendering is to encourage the Employer to provide the necessary early funding of the Work either by means of advance payments for mobilisation or by an immediate down payment once the Contract is signed or by use of an Imprest Account. All of these methods make it possible for the Contractor to avoid incorporating into his Tender large sums of money to cover interest charges which would otherwise be necessary if he alone was required to fund the Enterprise.

In doing his calculations about his financial capacity he must recognise also that, whereas the original Contract Period plus the Maintenance Period represented a given number of months or years locking up his investment, in the event of him being given an extension of time some of this money will remain locked up for periods longer than he contemplated. If this happens, he should remember that the issue of Variation Orders and other authorised extensions of the Time for Completion, provide him with the one way of including the additional costs of tied-up capital in new or varied rates.

employer – financial capacity

Employer's Financial Capacity – Whilst the construction of any Enterprise might appear attractive to the Contractor both by way of the status it might bring him or of the profit he might earn, he should always ensure, as far as possible, that the Employer has the financial capacity to fulfil his obligations to make payments in accordance with the Contract.

Even the largest of Employers, or indeed National Authorities, can have their financial position changed at most unexpected moments of time and this could leave the Contractor with a partially constructed Enterprise with little prospects of receiving any further monies.

If the Employer's funds have to be budgeted annually and the amount is uncertain in advance of the beginning of the year then it is very difficult for the Contractor to plan his work if financial restraints are likely to cause the tempo of the Works to be slowed down to match the finance available. In any case such changes in tempo will extend the Time for Completion and seriously inflate the final cost of the Enterprise.

It is therefore prudent for the Tendering Contractor to establish the financial capacity of the Employer involved and, because of the possibility of Certified payments not being honoured, he should, wherever possible, seek protection of his own Government-sponsored schemes which, under particular circumstances, will to some extent insure against default of payment by the Employer.

bond – performance

Performance Bond – In completing the Form of Tender the Contractor undertakes to obtain, if his Tender is accepted and if required, a guarantee or Bond approved by the Employer. Once the Tender is accepted and, being required to produce such a Bond, the Contractor is obliged to do so.

clause 10

If he then finds that it is not possible for him to obtain such a Bond he is in breach of Contract unless the Employer is prepared to accept another guarantee or other form of surety.

The Performance Bond can be called by the Employer should the Contractor fail to fulfil his obligations under the Contract and therefore the Contractor must be extremely cautious when agreeing the precise wording of the Bond with the Employer – particularly the terms which permit a call to be made on demand by the Employer and which do not limit the period of validity of the Bond.

Most Employers insist that if a Performance Bond is necessary it is payable "on demand without having to establish the reasons for calling the Bond" and this simply means that in the event of the Employer deciding to call in the Bond for whatever reason there is a positive obligation upon the Bank to make payment irrespective of any reason which made the Employer decide to call the Bond.

There is a distinct and separate relationship involved between the Parties – it is simply that the Bank or Insurance Company is obliged to honour the terms of the Bond on demand and is in no way concerned about the rights and wrongs of why the Bond is being called. Thereafter the Bank or Insurance Company has recourse to the Contractor for the full amount of the Bond and this puts the Contractor at considerable risk should he find that, whilst he and the Employer may be in dispute and even awaiting the outcome of any legal proceedings or arbitrations which might be in progress, the Employer suddenly exercises his contractual right and calls the Performance Bond.

Having paid the money to the Bank or Insurance Company the Contractor is well out of pocket and at a considerable disadvantage when negotiating the settlements of any dispute under the contract to say nothing of the possibility of being forced into liquidation – such bonds should be negotiated more favourably towards the Contractor or rejected.

care of works

Under the FIDIC Conditions of Contract the Contractor is required to take full care of the Works and insure jointly with the Employer against all losses or damage from whatever cause arising other than the Excepted Risks for all of his liabilities under the Contract both during the Construction Period and during the Period of Maintenance for certain matters which did not become the liability of the Employer upon the issue of a Completion Certificate. *clauses 8, 20, 2*

insurance

To do this he will insure the Works against all loss or damage, in the joint names of the Employer and the Contractor, generally under a Contractors All Risk Policy. It is not acceptable to take out the policy solely in the Contractor's name and merely note the involvement and interest of the Employer within this policy. *clause 21*

Such a Contractor's All Risks Policy should be written in its fullest terms but excluding the Excepted Risks. The amount insured by the policy would cover all "Works" and include both Permanent and Temporary Works together with the Constructional Plant (including that provided free by the Employer) and all other things brought to the Site by the Contractor for the purpose of executing the Works. The amount insured by the policy is likely to become even larger when taking into account inflation and Variations which are likely to arise. Because of this there needs to be a close understanding between the Contractor and his broker so that amounts insured and premiums to be paid can be reviewed from time to time, and appropriate adjustments made.

Insurances and especially Contractors All Risks Insurance need to be arranged by specially experienced brokers unless the Contractor already possesses within his own organisation an experienced and efficient employee knowledgeable on this subject generally and in particular concerning the country in which the Enterprise is being constructed. The Contractor should not rely upon his own experiences or views but seek guidance from such an Insurance broker.

The Contractor is further obliged to indemnify the Employer against all losses and claims in respect of injuries or damage to people, materials or property which may arise out of or in consequence of the execution and maintenance of the Works. This is with the exception of compensation or damage incurred by the Contractor, in respect of: *clause 22*

(1) Permanent use or occupation of the land by any part or whole of the Works.
(2) The Employer's right to execute work over, under or through any land involved with the Works.
(3) Injury or damage to property which is the unavoidable result of the execution or maintenance of the Works.

Injuries or damage to people or property resulting from an act of negligence of the Employer or others employed by him are indemnified by the Employer.

insurance – third party

The Contractor is required to insure against any liability for material or physical damage, loss or injury, which may occur to any property or to any persons including any employee of the Employer which arises out of the execution of the Works or in fulfilling all of his obligations under the Contract other than due to matters referred to in the proviso to Clause 22 (1).

clause 23

insurance – approval

It is a duty placed upon the Contractor that before commencing the execution of the Works he will insure against this liability and such an insurance shall be in terms approved by the Employer and shall be for an amount not less than that given in the Appendix to the Tender.

insurance – workmen

It is also the Contractor's responsibility to keep the Employer indemnified against all damage, compensation, claims proceedings etc., and expenses of whatever nature payable at Law in respect of any accident or injury to any Workmen employed by the Contractor or his Sub-Contractors except where occasioned and resulting from any actual default by the Employer or anyone employed by him – this is a Contractor's own policy which is not in the joint names of the Employer and himself.

clause 24

insurance – sub-contract

Insofar as any Sub-Contractor is concerned (this would include Nominated Sub-Contractors), the Contractor's obligation is such that it is not necessary to include anyone employed by the Sub-Contractor within the Contractor's own policy if the Sub-Contractor can produce an insurance policy which indemnifies both the Contractor and the Employer but such a policy and current premium payment certificate must be produced for examination by, and approval of, the Engineer when required.

insurance – employer take over

The matter of insurance is so important to the Employer that, should the Contractor fail to keep the insurance premiums fully paid, he retains the right to take out insurances himself and make payments himself in order to keep the policies alive or, if necessary, take out a suitable policy in his own name. Once having made a payment of any premium the Employer is entitled to deduct the amount he has paid from any monies due to him or, if no monies are due to the Contractor, he can regard this as a debt due to him.

clause 25

insurance – failure to insure

The importance of viewing the Tender Documents in their entirety and as a whole is most important to the Contractor. This is because of the variety and detail of information available and, because of this, suitable cross-checks should be made to ensure as far as possible that no error exists or that the Documents are not incomplete to such an extent as would affect the work.

tender – documents and drawings

At the time the Engineer issues the Tender Documents he includes one copy of all available tender and working drawings. These should accurately portray the intended construction of both Permanent and Temporary Works for which the Engineer is responsible and which are necessary for the Works to be constructed – later on, it will be seen the Contractor will be provided with two copies of all drawings free of charge and is required to retain one copy on site which should be available for use by the Engineer or anybody authorised by him – further copies required by the Contractor will be provided but at his own expense.

clauses 5, 6

drawings – disruption

Also at the time of Tender and even thereafter it might not be possible to have prepared each and every drawing in the fullest of detail but, once the Work has commenced, the Contractor is entitled to give notice to the Engineer if he feels that progress is likely to be delayed or disrupted unless further drawings are available. He must, however, recognise that the Engineer is to be given a reasonable time within which to produce them – it is no good asking for further drawings one day and to claim a delay to the Works if they are not available the following day.

clause 6

programme

Obviously, the construction programme provided by the Contractor is of considerable assistance in this matter in that it establishes the order of execution of the work and gives the Engineer an opportunity to produce the appropriate drawings in an organised and necessary sequence according to the progress rather than the order the Engineer thought might be appropriate to suit the needs of the Contractor.

clause 14

Once the work has commenced and should there be a failure or an inability

drawings –
delay

on the part of the Engineer to produce further drawings within a reasonable time *clause 6* and, if in consequence the Contractor suffers a delay or incurs additional costs, then these should be taken into account both for extra payment to the Contractor as well as giving cause for an extension to the Time for Completion to be awarded.

drawings –
further draw-
ings

Any further drawings, or instructions related to such drawings, as may become necessary, will, when issued by the Engineer, oblige the Contractor to be *clause 7* bound by them and carry them out exactly in the same manner as if he had received a written direction from the Engineer.

Whilst it is expected that sufficient drawings will be provided with the Tender Documents it sometimes happens that a number of them are not issued at that time but are known to be available at the Engineer's office for inspection – if this is so, then the Contractor in his own interest should visit the Engineer's office and give these drawings the same careful consideration as if they had been provided within the documents supplied to him – it is no excuse if the Contractor misses important information, which such drawings would have provided, to say he was unable to inspect them at the proper time.

specification

The Specification is part of the Contract Documents and generally gives standards for materials and workmanship required of the Contractor in the execution of the Works as well as information on a variety of other matters.

completion – in
specification

Often within the Specification will appear a number of items which require particular attention both at the Tender stage and during the construction of the Works. For example the Specification will set out the sequence of performance expected of the Contractor insofar as the Time of Completion of any Section of the Works is required within the completion of the Works as a whole or that the Employer will supply certain items of plant or equipment for the Permanent works together with the date when such items are expected to be made available on the Site.

codes of practice

Reference will be given to codes of practice or standard specifications concerning the nature of materials and the particular use of any materials which have been selected by the Engineer or the Employer for incorporation in the Works.

The Specification in general terms will set out the minimum standards required to satisfy the Engineer in the construction of the Works. If the Contractor finds it necessary to use a superior material in lieu of that specified or provide work to a higher standard than required this does not give him the right to any additional payment unless the improvement was the subject of change by a Variation Order.

tests – specifi-
cation

Within the Specification will be contained references to any Tests required under the Contract. Particular attention must be given to the performance of any Final Test which may be prescribed in that without this test being satisfactorily *clause 36* achieved the Contractor is not entitled to be given a Certificate of Completion even though physical construction of a Section or the Whole of the Works has been completed.

Many matters referred to in the proposals for the contents of Part II of the Conditions may be omitted from Part II in the Tender Documents and covered separately in the Specification.

bills of quan-
tities

The Form of Tender shows the Bills of Quantities as being a Contract Document but information as to their use or their formulation is extremely limited other than for the Tenderer to be advised that the quantities are "estimated" only and the rates will be used as appropriate when evaluating Variation Orders *clause 55* issued by the Engineer.

It is important to the Contractor that as early as possible during the Tender stage he checks the Bills of Quantities against the Specification and the available drawings to see that there is no major error which will in any way influence his method of pricing – if this happens he should refer his findings to the Engineer at the time.

Whilst a change in quantities itself presents no difficulties when evaluating the work, it is not possible under the Contract to claim that an unusually large change in quantities gives the Contractor an entitlement to additional payment unless arising from a Variation Order.

It would however be reasonable to suggest that although the quantities have been "estimated" the amounts given in the Bills of Quantities prepared by the Engineer should be as close as reasonably possible to the actual quantities formed later in the Works as constructed. Should the final quantities vary considerably from those shown at the time of Tender the Contractor might argue that the Documents were misleading to a degree which affected the balance of his pricing and that this might give him an entitlement to additional payment.

bills of quan-
tities
The Bills of Quantities themselves provide the Contractor with an opportunity to price individually described items of work in any manner he chooses, but in so doing he must be aware that whilst remaining responsible for the physical construction of the Works he will be paid only in accordance with the Bills of Quantities both during the interim stages of construction and when the Final Account is prepared.

clause 55

It can be argued that each unit rate itself is a lump sum unit in its own right and that the Contractor has priced the Bills by considering each item individually in its own context. However, some Contractors prefer to construct a Tender on a different philosophy altogether and to let "time" become the predominant feature and for all the attendant resources of labour and Constructional Plant etc., to be given a time-based cost value and their considerations do not relate the costs solely to an activity or quantity of work by trades. If the Tender is prepared on such a time basis it means that the Tender Price is prepared on an overall conception of the Works and not by specifically pricing each unit of work as described. Under these circumstances rates or prices set against the Bill items become related to apparent reasonableness rather than individual competence and are often weighted to give an advantageous Cash Flow.

pricing
The actual method of preparation of the Tender itself may differ between Contractors but they are entitled to distribute the profit and overhead elements of their work in any manner they so wish and, therefore, the level of prices or rates is set to suit their own particular purpose.

cash flow
Whilst this can give the advantage of an early and positive Cash Flow and, indeed possible gain if changes of quantities come out in the Contractor's favour, there is always the possibility of a disadvantage arising should a Variation Order be given which could reduce substantially the quantity of work in any item carrying a disproportionately high level of profit or overhead. Reductions in value caused by these happenings cannot be recovered without great difficulty.

method of
measurement
Method of Measurement – Whilst the information given in respect of Bills of Quantities might be considered somewhat vague, information concerning the Method of Measurement is even more so. Other than stating that the measurement itself will be on a net basis, notwithstanding any local custom, no further details are given.

clause 57

It is reasonable to suggest that the preparation of the Bills of Quantities and particularly the content of the individual items it contains must have been prepared with the intention that the various measurements concerning trades or activities are taken in certain ways to ensure that the descriptions are related to the manner in which the work so described will be constructed and thus can be priced accordingly.

Some countries already recognise this need and have adopted their own Standard Method of Measurement to be applied to various trades – if such standards are given as part of the Contract Document then arguments about the correct procedure for measurement for each item are minimised.

If, however, no such Standard Method of Measurement is stated within the Conditions then it is of importance to the Contractor to seek out and understand the customs of the country in which the work is being constructed. In the absence of such understanding he may assess the value of work performed under an established system of a Standard Method with which he is familiar and, indeed, thinks is applicable. However he may discover himself eventually in the unfortunate position of being paid only according to the customs of measurement applicable to local conditions which might be very different from those erroneously assumed at the time of Tender.

If the Specification or the Instructions to Tenderers do not contain sufficient information to enable the Contractor to relate objectively the quantities and descriptions within an accepted or predetermined form of Method of Measurement then he should refer the matter to the Engineer as soon as possible in order to make certain that when pricing the Bills he is wholly informed about the intentions of the descriptions of work and to the precise method of measuring and recording dimensions.

The Royal Institution of Chartered Surveyors in England have issued a publication entitled *Principles of Measurement (International) for Works of Construction – 1979*, which provides a useful guide to the manner by which such work should be presented for pricing.

In having the Bills of Quantities available and possible ways by which the work is to be measured the Contract then states who shall be responsible for the Measurement of the Works and how and when it will be done.   *clause 56*

measurement – timing

Once the construction of the work is proceeding and, unless it is stated otherwise, it is the Engineer who is responsible for determining the value of the work done by measurements and, when doing so, he can call upon the Contractor to attend. If the Contractor does not attend then the measurements taken by the Engineer shall be deemed to be correct.

records

If it is necessary for records to be prepared and drawings to be provided in respect of Permanent Works in order that they can be measured then it is the Engineer's Representatives' responsibility to prepare these but he can call upon   *clause 56* the Contractor to attend the measurement and will give him the opportunity of agreeing such records so prepared on the Engineer's behalf.

If the Contractor does not attend with the Engineer's Representatives when requested the records provided by the Engineer's Representatives are to be taken as correct but, if the Contractor examines them and does not agree with them, then he must within fourteen days notify the Engineer that he is dissatisfied with the records and drawings and state specifically in which respect he disagrees with them.

This clause, as such, only defines responsibility for measurement and does not state specifically when this will be carried out – however, the measurement and recording of work performed is an ongoing situation starting from the time when physical work on Site commenced until the last day of its completion – if this did not happen then the preparation of the Final Account would rely only on memories.

site visit

Up to this point the consideration being given by the Contractor to the various matters referred to above has possibly been carried out in the confines of his own offices so he should now find himself contemplating a visit to Site, and the   *clause 11* team which will support him in his investigations.

The composition of the team will obviously vary with each Enterprise depending upon the size and complexity of the Works proposed and will be guided by the experiences of the individual Contractors involved. It would prob-

site visit – team

ably comprise the Project Manager elect, a Civil Engineer Estimator who will be seeking quotations and guide prices from local suppliers and contractors; possibly an in-house Geologist; and if circumstances so dictate a Medical Doctor who will study the environment of the Site and any medical hazards likely to arise in addition to seeking knowledge of the availability of hospital services and medical facilities for both indigenous and expatriate staff.

site visit – purpose

The visit to Site is possibly one of the largest items of expenditure incurred when preparing a Tender because it will often involve a team of highly paid people with specialised knowledge of their respective subjects.

The purpose of such a visit is to ensure that the Contractor is fully acquainted with all the local circumstances which can affect his Tender. Because a Site visit is "deemed" to have been made there is no requirement for the Contractor to visit the Site; if he wishes he can rely solely upon his imagination and book knowledge when pricing the Bills of Quantities. It is not obligatory to visit the Site   *clause 11* according to the FIDIC Conditions of Contract. Nevertheless he must visit the Site if the Instructions to Tenderers require this to be done.

During a Site visit he should pay particular attention to a number of important factors which could cause him considerable inconvenience and expense if not given a proper study before the submission of his Tender.

When visiting the Site the Contractor will find Part II – used as an aide memoire – most helpful in giving subject headings for those matters which should receive his attention. The following observations in general cover subjects likely to arise:

(1) The Contractor will have firmly in his mind that he is to be responsible for the execution of the Works and for the provision of all things necessary in connection therewith: labour, supervision, materials, constructional plant, leasing of land etc., and it is because of this his visit to Site will be the prime source for obtaining specific information which will particularly effect these responsibilities.

labour

clauses 8, 34, 35

(2) He will make himself fully acquainted with the availability of local labour and craftsmen and with the local laws, customs, holidays, religions, and rates of pay concerning their employment – he must also make provision for either their accommodation on Site or their transportation to and from the Site.

laws – local

clause 34

(3) Likewise he will make detailed enquiries about the availability of materials and make certain they satisfy the particular requirements of the Specification – for example in respect of contracts requiring large supplies of stone for road-making it is not unusual for a Contractor to take an option on a quarry with the expectation of obtaining the Contract but will expect to be able to sell it to the successful Contractor if he fails to secure the Contract himself.

materials

clause 8

(4) Whilst he is on Site he should make contact with the Bank with which he will deal if awarded the Contract and arrange with the local Manager for the remittance of funds to and from his own country and for any overdraft required to finance the Contract. He should also make detailed enquiries about the availability of local currencies and this will become important to him after he has completed his calculations for the Tender when he will be aware of the extent of his requirements for both local and foreign currencies.

financing

currency

clauses 60, 72

(5) The repatriation of profits is possibly one of the most important matters concerning the Contractor in that whilst it is possible for him to construct the Works with skill and make a profit he must establish at the time of tendering whether it is worth his while to submit his Tender should it not be possible to remit a sufficient percentage of his profit wheresoever he wishes.

profits – repatriation

Because the Contractor is a commercial and trading concern and is constantly seeking to improve his status with increasingly better dividend payments it is a reality of life that unless funds can be transferred to the Contractor's Head Office for distribution to shareholders, then working in any other country will generally lose its attraction.

(6) A Site visit should establish the availability and location of supplies of water, electrical energy and fuel. Other facilities to be established are site security, access to site from ports, airfields and rail heads, telephone services and such like. The Contractor should make clear in his Tender his understanding of the manner by which water and electricity supply are to be distributed around the Site – it is one thing to say that the Employer will accept responsibility for the free supply of water and electrical energy for the Contract but the responsibility for the cost of the necessary distribution network is another.

supplies – utilities local

security

energy – distribution

(7) Whilst he is on Site he will consider the accommodation for any expatriate staff and should make necessary enquiries concerning visas and work permits. Very often the visas and work permits are arranged by the Employer himself as he is generally more in contact with the local authorities who issue them – or he will assist wherever possible in their

staff – expatriate

procurement. Care should be taken to establish the time scale existing in the country or embassies abroad for the arrangement of visas and work permits.

It is desirable to study the status of all staff and ensure that the accommodation to be provided will be equal to such status given. The question of who is to be the legal owner of such accommodation when the Contract is completed has also to be determined.

medical and educational facilities

(8) He should study the availability of medical facilities and, if inadequate, he should consider making his own arrangements by including the cost of medical staff and attendant facilities as part of his Tender. The need for schools for any indigenous and expatriate children on Site must be studied at the same time.

sub-contractors – local

(9) Because some work might be performed under Sub-Contract he should meet local Sub-Contractors and seek to establish suitable quotations with conditions under which they would work for him – it may be through them that he should be able to improve his knowledge of the probability factors of the risks he will be accepting if his bid is successful and thus be able to assess his potential exposure more accurately.

offices – off-site

(10) He should assess the need to establish an office off-site and all the costs attendant thereto for the purpose of administering business affairs which are not necessarily directly involved in the construction processes but are essential to ensure a rapid and efficient flow of labour and materials and to expedite the importation of constructional plant, materials and equipment.   *clause 42*

site diary – records

(11) The Contractor should be aware at all times that it is very important to keep adequate and complete site records even of this preliminary Site visit itself – diaries, daywork sheets, labour and plant returns, programmes, Engineers' instructions, weather reports, accidents, dangerous occurrences, etc., in anticipation of potential disputes and arbitration. Equally it is very necessary to appreciate that local legislation may require the retention of labour records – time sheets, payrolls, and the like and all financial, accounting and legal agreements with suppliers, sub-contractors, personnel etc. for many years after the completion of the Works. Thus consideration must be given in the tender price for the costs of preserving all these records not only during the contract period but possibly for up to fifteen or more years after the issue of the Maintenance Certificate – this being often necessary for the negotiating of the final tax clearance.

Modern methods of recording such as microfilm and microfiche should be borne in mind together with the need for a document store which is fire proof, thief-proof and vermin-proof.

geological data

(12) Probably the most important matter to him during the visit will be the reconciliation of the geological data, which the Employer has provided, with the Site conditions as physically examined by him, and whilst it might please him to sink a number of test or trial pits to evaluate probable earthmoving outputs, there is no obligation to embark upon a deep probe survey of the soil conditions at his own expense because he is only obliged to inspect and examine the sub-soil conditions so far as practicable.   *clause 11*

geological report

If he becomes aware of an obvious discrepancy between the geological information provided by the Employer and the actual conditions encountered on the Site it is incumbent upon him to inform the Engineer about what he has discovered and where conflict or ambiguity might exist with or within the Geological Report.

A visual examination of the Site over its whole area will include observations of the surrounding topography as well as any open excavations provided by local industries which rely upon the natural geology of the surrounding areas; e.g. quarries would obviously indicate the nature of the rock in the area. Local agri-

public utilities

culture with fields producing crops should give an understanding of the local ground conditions also. Information should be sought about the position of underground and surface services of any Public Utilities which might need removing or re-positioning during the construction period and the cost for so doing allowed in the Tender.

mineral rights

The Instructions to Tenderers may include reference to the ownership and possible use of minerals, particularly sand and rock suitable for making concrete, and whether the Contractor is to make payment to the Employer for the use of such materials or they are to be given as free issue to him, either as excavated by the Contractor or delivered to him without charge.

programme

Unless required by the Instructions to Tenderers to submit a programme with the Tender the Conditions of Contract do not require this to be done. However, it is obviously sensible for a Contractor to provide a programme as part of his Tender, particularly if he wishes to claim additional monies if and when his anticipated programme of construction is disrupted in any way or in the circumstances when a large number of Variation Orders are issued to him which interrupt his intended sequence of working and cause a major disruption and heavy financial expenditure.

clause 14

The programme as supplied by the Contractor forecasts the progress anticipated and illustrates the manner by which, and the time in which, he will construct the Works, and the plant he will use in so doing. Sometimes a programme so submitted will show a Time for Completion shorter than the Contractual Time for Completion but, if the Contractor fails to complete at the programmed date yet nevertheless completes within the Contract Time for Completion, then there is no penalty by way of Liquidated Damages. Whilst the Contractor would no doubt benefit by an earlier completion there is no contractual obligation upon him so to do just because his Tender programme might show this – his only contractual obligation is to complete within the Contract Time for Completion plus any Extensions of Time.

Other purposes of the Tender programme are to provide dates when certain works are to begin and be completed, and dates relating to the provision of drawings and the expected delivery dates for Special Plant provided by the Employer.

payment

The subject of Certificate and Payment is one of the greatest importance to the Contractor and is treated extensively either in the Specification or within the Contract Documents by Part II Clause 60.

clause 60

The information provided under this heading should deal with matters concerning advance payments, and how and when they should be made together with the method to be adopted for repayments – repayments can be agreed as a percentage of the value of work performed, a fixed amount on a monthly basis or on the basis of any other mutually agreed formula.

payment advance/refund

Although not included in the evaluation of the Works as performed it is nevertheless the responsibility of the Engineer to make deductions of any agreed repayment or advance payment in the Certificate of Payment he issues to the Employer – it should not be left to the Employer to apply such adjustment himself upon receipt of the Engineer's Certificate.

measurement

Notwithstanding the duty of the Engineer to measure the Works it is customary for the Contractor to submit to the Engineer an evaluation of the Works executed on a monthly basis; this is often referred to as an "invoice" or "claim" from the Contractor but should be referred to more correctly as the Contractor's "Application for Payment".

Nevertheless for payment purposes the value of the Works executed is given solely in the Certificate of the Engineer and it is only the Engineer's Certificate which states the amount due to the Contractor and it is on the basis of this Certificate alone that the Employer is obliged to pay.

certificate – payment

Such a Certificate by the Engineer will include the value of Permanent Works executed and of those Temporary Works which are separately identifiable as such in the Bills of Quantities – it will also include advance payments for materials on site as may be certified by the Engineer but appertaining only to the Permanent Works being performed – there is no such advance to be made in respect of the temporary works or temporary materials unless this should be so determined in the Instructions to Tenderers or in the Specification.

The percentage or amount of Retention Money should be given in the document or within the Instruction to Tenderers as a percentage of the value of Works performed, usually with a limiting percentage which when once reached will not *retention* be increased further. Part II Clause 60 should also describe how the Retention Monies will be released and, in general, this would be for one half to be released at the same time as the issue of an appropriate Certificate of Completion and for the *clause 60* other half being released as and when any defined Period of Retention has expired.

The release of the second half of the Retention should have no relationship with the issue of the Maintenance Certificate but is done on a time basis only. *retention* However, some of the Retention Money may still be retained pending completion *(release)* of unfinished work which can still be in progress after the Maintenance Period itself has expired.

In the case where the Work is done in Sections, each Section will be considered separately, but the release of the remaining half of the Retention Money *works – sections* should be made after the expiry of the Maintenance Period of the last Section completed.

Part II Clause 60 requires information about the method of correction or the withholding of Certificates by the Engineer to be given as part of the Instructions *certificate –* to Tenderers. Any Interim Certificate of Payment which the Engineer issues can *clause 60* *withholding* be changed if considered necessary during the course of the Work.

Information about the frequencies of Interim Payments and the minimum amount payable should be given in the Information to Tenderers and the Con- *payments –* tractor should ensure that he does not enter into Sub-Contract Agreements which *interim* require him to make payment for work before he receives appropriate payments himself from the Employer.

Details of currencies required in the various proportions necessary for funding the Contract and applicable rates of exchange should be included as part *payment – cur-* of the Tender, either under this heading or within the Contractor's Tender *rencies* Letter. *clauses 60, 72*

The Contractor will recognise that adjustments in currency values, both local and foreign, or the fluctuation in the rates of wages and materials and statutory changes of customs and import duties, due to legal ordinances etc., will all need to be given a definition within this clause and how they will affect the Contract Price. Whilst such adjustments are not part of the measurement of the Works as performed, they are part nevertheless of the Value of such Works and *clause 70* are within the Engineer's authority to certify appropriate payment.

At this point the Contractor's visit to Site is complete and he should now be in possession of sufficient and the fullest of necessary information to prepare and formulate his Tender build-up – and with the working programme it should enable him to isolate various costs, establish unit rates and reach the Tender Price.

Before actually completing the Tender, the Contractor should remind himself that it is he, and not the Employer or the Engineer, who is deemed to have *tender price* satisfied himself before Tendering about the correctness and sufficiency of his Tender for the Works and that the rates and prices which he quotes will cover all of his obligations under the Contract in all matters and all things necessary for the proper execution and maintenance of the Works.

In other words it is at this moment of time that he must make certain completely that the Tender Price is the one he intends to submit and nothing has been omitted or inserted incorrectly which will put him at undue risk. It is important that the Tender is signed by a properly authorised person on behalf of the Con- *clause 8* tractor.

If the Contractor is obliged or wishes to withdraw his Tender this must be done before the date when Tenders are due to be opened and the procedure is laid down in the Instructions to Tenderers as to how this should be done. It is again of the utmost importance to follow these instructions precisely if the Contractor intends to withdraw because, if he does not do so, his Tender will remain as a valid offer and will be open to acceptance possibly against his wishes.

acceptance of tender

Acceptance – The Contractor likes to know if he is the lowest bidder and after waiting with interest to know the position of his Tender he is particularly pleased if advised that he is the lowest. Often he will undergo a sensation of doubt and trepidation in case there should have been an error somewhere within his calculations and sometimes becomes emotional if he hears that not only is his Tender the lowest but that it is the lowest by a considerable amount.

tender – lowest

As the lowest bidder, or often within the lowest three, the Contractor will be invited to the office of the Engineer to give detailed explanations of any qualifications and, wherever possible, to remove them or evaluate them so that his Tender can be related finally to others and any adjustments made to his Tender Price.

If still remaining the lowest bidder it is not uncommon as a sequel to this meeting with the Engineer for the Contractor to receive a letter from the Engineer advising him of the Employer's intention of placing this Contract with the Contractor – not always immediately, but in due course, giving a possible date when this will be done and of the date when an Instruction to Commence is likely to be given.

letter of intent

This letter is referred to as a "Letter of Intent" and in effect means precisely what it says – no Contract exists between the Employer and the Contractor at this stage – even the consideration of giving an "intention" is not sufficient to form a Contract – therefore should the Contractor decide to start planning and make positive arrangements with staff and with the placing of orders in advance of receiving an official acceptance he does so entirely at his own risk and cost.

However, should there be a written undertaking established between the Employer and the Contractor within the Letter of Intent to the effect that any action he takes in this matter will be at the Employer's cost if the Contractor does not secure the Contract, then the Contractor is at little risk and has a claim recoverable in law on the basis of being paid the reasonable costs incurred or on a quantum meriut basis as it is known should no other form of payment have been previously agreed – with no such understanding he does everything at his own risk and cost.

2. CONSTRUCTION

General Responsibilities – Upon receipt of the Employer's formal written acceptance of the Contractor's offer, the Employer and the Contractor are deemed to have entered into a Contract. It is suitable at this time for the Contractor to recall his general responsibilities which include the proper execution of the construction and maintenance of the Works, the provision of all labour, supervision, materials, constructional plant and all other things either of a temporary or permanent nature which he requires in undertaking the construction of the Works and the obligation to ensure completion, which, if he fails to achieve at the agreed time, will incur the payment of Liquidated Damages.

Contractor's general responsibilities

clause 8

He also should remember that in undertaking the construction of the Works he will accept full responsibility for the adequacy, stability and safety of all site operations and methods of construction – providing that he will not be responsible, unless so stated in the Tender, for the design and the specification of the Permanent Works themselves, and for those Works which have been designed and specified as Temporary Works by the Engineer.

In particular he should remember that whereas the Engineer designed the Works to be in a satisfactory and competent state when ultimately completed it is left to the Contractor to ensure that the Works are sufficiently safe and maintained during the various stages of construction until a successful completion has been achieved.

Works – temporary

Certain Temporary Works are expressly identified in the Contract as being designed by the Engineer and as such are not part of the Contractor's responsibilities. The Contractor is responsible for the safety and adequacy of all Temporary Works he designs.

clause 1

Two categories of Temporary Works exist – those designed by the Engineer, and those by the Contractor – each has a further classification differentiating between "Temporary – but being subsequently removed" and "Temporary but left in position".

Finally, the Contractor accepts the fact that the Engineer is not required to do his job for him and certainly not to fulfil any of his obligations under the Contract. The Contractor's problems are his alone and whilst most Engineers are more than helpful during difficult periods the Engineer should remember always there are limits of involvements which must not be exceeded other than at his own risk.

agreement
Agreement – Shortly after acceptance, the Contractor will be called upon to enter into and execute a Contract Agreement which itself will bind together all the various elements of the Contract Documents and will be signed by both *clause 9* Parties.

In countries where companies are required to sign Contracts under seal a Contract so signed will carry different obligations from those of a Contract signed without seal. In English Law the distinction is that there is a legal responsibility placed upon the Contractor for a period of twelve years, compared with six years when not under Seal, within such times he must accept liability for errors in the performance of his work which might subsequently be discovered after completion.

commencement
Commencement – Assuming that the Contractor has received an acceptance of his Tender and not just a Letter of Intent he will anticipate an Instruction to Commence Work from the Engineer accompanied by a communication from the *clause 41* Employer permitting him to enter the Site.

The Instruction to Commence from the Engineer must be written and it constitutes an order obligating the Contractor to commence work within the interval named in the Appendix to the Form of Tender which, to all intents and purposes, can be regarded as a mobilisation period. The starting date of the Time for Completion follows the last day of such interval.

If the Contractor does not start work within this period and cannot offer an acceptable reason for so doing then the Engineer will give him a specific notice to commence. If the Contractor does not commence within the following twenty-eight days then the Employer will consider the Contractor to be in default and can implement a remedy against the Contractor by occupying the Site and doing the work himself at the Contractor's expense.

Such an action does not void the Contract, in that the Contractor is not released from any of his obligations or liabilities, but it certainly puts him in the invidious position of meeting all manner of charges which in all probability will be far in excess of the cost of the work had he undertaken it himself, or, possibly, of the value of the work assessed by the application of the rates and prices in the Bills of Quantities.

site – not available
If the Contractor is unable to proceed simply because the Employer does not make those parts of the Site available which are required to commence and proceed with the execution of the work and if it is not possible to put forward reasonable proposals as to how this problem will be overcome, the Contractor is entitled to give written notice to the Engineer for possession of any further parts of the Site he requires. If these are not available then the Contractor is entitled to be *clause 42* paid the costs arising from the delay caused by the failure on the part of the Employer to provide access to and possession of the Site, and also may be given an extension to the Time of Completion if considered appropriate by the Engineer.

employer – own plant
However, where the Contract is such that the Employer is to provide essential plant or equipment at particular dates, then failure by him to do so constitutes a breach of Contract and makes the Time for Completion no longer valid – this is because the Contract does not treat a situation involving delay in the provision of plant and equipment in the same manner as a delay in occupation of the Site. If a delay in the provision of Plant or Equipment occurs then, provided the Contractor conducts himself properly thereafter in expeditiously executing the Works as is his obligation, he should recover all additional costs incurred without

being at risk of Liquidated Damages being levied against him.

Site diary

Site Diary – from the date of commencement of any operations on the Site or even before that – say whilst visiting the Site during the Pre-Tender stage – a Contractor is well advised to introduce a Site diary and to instruct his staff to complete a full record each day without exception – inclusive of holidays and other days when the Site might be closed. A list of suitable headings covering the information and data to be recorded is given in the Appendix – the example so given is not exclusive – there may well be other items to be added to suit special circumstances – and it is more appropriate to the needs of a Contractor. Nevertheless the Engineer is advised also to keep a similar diary, although he may prefer to use a different set of subject headings to suit his purpose.

Labour – employment

Employer of Labour – Having been given the Order to Commence, the Contractor becomes responsible for the proper conduct by all his Employees – including both Nominated and domestic Sub-Contractors – in the observance of Statutes, Ordinances, Government Regulations and Orders, particularly concerning the introduction of alcohol or drugs on to the Site, and for ensuring that nobody becomes involved in matters of the supplying of arms or ammunition whether by gift or barter.   *clause 34*

Religions

He must, in particular, recognise the religious festivals, days of rest and religious and other customs appropriate to the labour force in his employment. He should have been aware before the time of Tender that religious festivals or fasts might continue for a long period and often effectively stop work or reduce productivity. Such matters do not entitle the Contractor to any additional remuneration or give cause for extending the Time for Completion as a Special Circumstance unless introduced subsequent to the acceptance of the Tender.

Local government sanitation

The Contractor is obliged to comply with all regulations made by the Government or local medical or sanitary authorities in dealing with outbreaks of illness of an epidemic nature and is required to carry out all instructions as may be issued by such authorities. Whilst this might be considered a special circumstance entitling the Contractor to an Extension of Time, there is no suitable clause within the Conditions of Contract which transfers the financial outcome to the Employer, unless it can be found that its origin lies in one of the Excepted Risks or Special Risks.   *clause 34*

Riots

The Contractor is required to take all reasonable precautions to prevent unlawful, riotous or disorderly conduct by his Employees – including those of all Sub-Contractors – and for the preservation of peace and protection of persons and property in the neighbourhood wherein the Works are being constructed. This is an extremely onerous obligation to place upon the Contractor but it should be noted that what he is required to do is "at all times take all reasonable precautions to prevent" such disorderly conduct.   *clauses 20, 34, 65*

Programme

Following the acceptance of his Tender the Contractor is obliged to submit a programme to the Engineer giving the order of procedure in which he proposes to carry out the Works – this programme should be submitted to the Engineer for approval within the number of days stated in the Instructions to Tenderers or Specification.   *clause 14*

Such a programme will give a general description of the methods the Contractor intends to adopt for the Construction of the Works and will be the basis on which the Engineer and the Employer organise the provision of drawings, and the availability of parts of the Site and finances. If it is necessary for this programme to be changed subsequently to suit the Contractor's convenience, then provided it still fulfils his obligation for completion at the appointed time, the Engineer would find it difficult not to give his approval to such a revised programme.

Programme – revised

However, the Engineer has the right to seek a revised programme himself if it should appear at any time that the Contractor's progress towards completion does not conform with the approved programme and, at the request of the Engineer, the Contractor must produce a further revised programme showing necessary changes and modifications whereby the Completion of the Works will be achieved on time.   *clause 14*

The involvement of the Engineer or his Representatives in the approval of any programme, or indeed the giving of particulars which form part of this programme, or his agreement to the arrangements or methods which the Contractor proposes to adopt for the execution of the work will not relieve the Contractor of any of his responsibilities under the Contract.

Change of Programme – Any revised programme should give more detailed information about the order of procedure as well as of the manner in which the Contractor intends to carry out the Works, but it must be remembered that it is the Contractor who is responsible for progress and not the Engineer, but, if the Engineer considers that the actual progress of the Works at any time does not conform to the earlier programmes, which he has approved, then he can ask for yet further revised programmes to be given to him showing modifications to ensure a successful Completion on Time.

This presents rather an unusual situation in that there is no specific requirement for the Contractor to submit a programme which the Engineer likes but which the Contractor does not and therefore, should this situation occur, the Contractor might claim an Extension of Time because of the delay in obtaining approval. However, there are no appropriate means whereby the Contractor can claim the costs which he might lose because of any such delay.

Obviously, a "programme" can mean different things to many people and will vary in presentation from the simple bar chart, which expresses time factors on a lineal basis, to the more sophisticated critical path programme which, more often than not, will be produced by computer.

Whilst it is an obligation for the Contractor to provide a programme to the Engineer, unless the format of such a programme is specified in a particular manner in the Instructions to Tenderers or Specification, the Contractor has the right to present it in whichever form he prefers. In presenting it to the Engineer the Contractor is seeking only the Engineer's approval of its content and not its manner of presentation.

programme – method

If it happens that the Engineer should decide that a bar chart programme presented by the Contractor is not what he wants, and that he would prefer or wish that the programme be shown on a critical path basis then the Contractor is entitled to payment for providing such a programme and for the payment of any ongoing costs which such a programme entails.

progress – rate of

Rate of Progress – If the Contractor is proceeding with the Works at a rate of progress which, in the opinion of the Engineer, is too slow to ensure completion by the proper date the Engineer can notify the Contractor in writing of such opinion. Upon receipt of such a notice the Contractor must seek approval of the *clause 46* Engineer to the steps which are necessary to expedite progress and Completion on Time.

work – ex-pedition

The Contractor is not entitled to any extra payments for such expedition because this is not a Variation Order. If it is necessary for this acceleration to become effective and for the Contractor to work at nights or on Sundays or on *clause 45* other locally recognised days of rest then such permission will not unreasonably be refused by the Engineer.

plant – construction

Plant for the Works – All constructional plant, temporary works and materials provided by the Contractor, once they are on Site, are deemed to be exclusively intended for the Works and the Contractor is not permitted to remove them *clause 53* without the consent of the Engineer, which should not be withheld unreasonably.

plant – completion

When the Works have been completed, and in this context it means when a Completion Certificate has been issued, the Contractor is obliged to remove from Site all constructional plant, Temporary Works and unused materials which remain – this would be with the exception of items which are still necessary to complete the outstanding works during the Maintenance Period.

plant – excepted risks

plant – special risks

The Employer does not undertake any liability for risk of damage to any of the above except as may be incurred by the occurrence of the Excepted and Special Risks which generally are not insurable.

customs – clearance

When the Employer undertakes to assist the Contractor in obtaining clearance through customs for constructional plant and the like his obligation is restricted to "assisting" – the involvement of the Employer arises because he is considered to be in a more advantageous position to instigate processes which are necessary and far more aware of the procedures and methods of expedition applicable to local customs than is the Contractor. *clause 53*

ınt – re-port

The Contractor should be aware of some of the pitfalls of re-exportation, especially when customs duty has been waived on importation under guarantee of re-exportation at the end of the Works. Many items of plant, equipment and materials become lost, are stolen, are incorporated in the Works, and spare parts are built into items of plant during repairs and so on. A too rigid bureaucracy can make things very difficult when the day comes to re-export that which was imported without payment of customs duties several years ago. Equally it is not always possible to sell plant and equipment at the end of the contract without having paid the duty first and the temptation arises to take the re-exportable goods through the port of entry and dump them in the sea when the cost of re-exportation and shipping is in excess of the written-down value of the goods and there is no immediate use for them in the country of origin.

Because the re-export of constructional plant is often difficult the Employer undertakes to assist the Contractor whenever required in obtaining any necessary Governmental consent for the re-export of such constructional plant and of its removal. Again this does not place the Employer under a greater obligation than to "assist" – he does not guarantee that he will obtain Government consent and the Contractor has no argument against the Employer if his assistance does not prove successful. *clause 53*

terials – ap-val

Approval of Materials – the fact that assistance is given by the Employer to the Contractor to bring to Site the materials and constructional plant does not imply that the Employer or the Engineer approves such materials or constructional plant simply because the Employer is involved. This does not prevent the Engineer from rejecting any materials or plant which he considers to be unsuitable. *clause 54*

ysical con-tion

Physical Conditions – When preparing his Tender the Contractor will have taken into account all those things which were reasonable to have been foreseen, in his opinion by an experienced Contractor, either as a direct consequence of his Site examination or within his experience of the probability of certain physical circumstances arising. *clause 12*

He is protected under the Contract to the extent that, should he encounter any physical conditions or artificial obstructions which in "his opinion" could not have been reasonably foreseen by an experienced Contractor, then he is entitled to Additional Payment and Extensions of Time – provided always that the Engineer agrees with his view and is given written notice at the time the Contractor encounters such conditions.

Whilst there is a qualification to the effect that such physical conditions do not include climatic conditions on Site this must be read in conjunction with the Excepted Risks clause which makes reference to "any such operations of the forces of nature as an experienced Contractor could not foresee or reasonably make provisions for or to insure against". This means that the occurrence of any adverse climatic conditions, whether foreseeable as such or not, would not permit a claim under Clause 12 but if, of considerable magnitude, would receive more proper attention under Clause 20. *clauses 12, 20*

structions – gineer

The Contractor's entitlement to be paid under Clause 12 relies upon complying with the Instructions which the Engineer may issue to him – or upon the taking by the Contractor of any proper and reasonable measures, subsequently approved by the Engineer, in the absence of specific instructions from the Engineer. The Engineer can issue instructions as to how to overcome the adverse physical conditions or he can leave it to the Contractor to do whatever is necessary according to his own judgement and formulate a decision upon the matter at a later date. *clause 12*

finition – ysical con-ions

It should be noted that the wording of Clause 12 refers only to encountering physical conditions, etc., which could not have been reasonably foreseen by an experienced Contractor and it is only in the marginal notes that the word "adverse" appears. The reader's attention is directed to the clause on Definitions

which states that such marginal notes shall not be deemed to be part of the Con- *clause 1*
ditions of Contract or taken into consideration in interpreting or in the construction of the Contract.

If, however, the ground conditions are found to be much easier than foreseen
at the time the Engineer prepared the Bills of Quantities or by the Contractor
when examining the Site, e.g. encountering rock much easier to work than the
geological information and data indicated, the Engineer is not permitted thereby
to claim "unforeseen physical conditions" on behalf of the Employer and so seek
a reduction in any rates or prices. The Engineer is not able to use this clause in
that it applies only to those matters which an experienced Contractor should
have foreseen.

Unforeseen physical conditions or artificial obstructions can cover a large
number of possibilities and could range from cases where water tables are found
at unexpected levels to underground obstructions caused by ancient mine work-
ings, which were not shown on any available map. All of such cases should be
compared with the geological information provided by the Employer and used by
the Contractor when preparing his Tender because the Tender "shall be deemed
to have been based upon such data" and should have been taken into account
when the Contractor visited the Site.

When encountering physical conditions, which could not have been reasonably foreseen by an experienced Contractor, the Contractor must remember that
it is up to him to instigate the processes whereby he receives additional Payment
and Extensions of Time. It is not a matter which the Engineer is required to acti-
vate. This is totally opposite to the issuing of a Variation Order which the Engineer and not the Contractor is obliged to initiate.

payment – claim
A claim by the Contractor for Additional Payment to be made to him must
satisfy two main criteria. The principal one is that he incurs additional cost.
Secondly, the circumstances in the opinion of the Contractor could not have been
reasonably foreseen by an experienced Contractor. If these criteria are satisfied *clause 60*
and, provided he gives notice to the Engineer at the appropriate time, then Additional Payment and an Extension of Time should be given.

Suspension of the Works – It is only on the receipt of a written order from the
Engineer that the Contractor may suspend the progress of the Works for such
suspension of
work
time and in such a way as the Engineer may consider necessary and not when the
Contractor might wish to do so. During such a suspension the Contractor is *clause 40*
obliged to properly protect and secure the Works as considered necessary by the
Engineer and the extra cost incurred by the Contractor for so doing will be paid
by the Employer unless such suspension:

(1) Was already provided within the Contract or the programme in which
    case the costs of suspension were deemed to have been included in the Con-
    tract price.
(2) Has arisen by some default on behalf of the Contractor himself.
(3) Has become necessary for reasons of climatic conditions on the Site. It
    should be noted that the Suspension of the Works through climatic con-
    ditions must be considered further in detail because the Excepted Risks
    require the Contractor to include as his liability those climatic conditions
    involving "the operation of the forces of nature as an experienced contrac-
    tor could foresee or reasonably to have insured against" and therefore,
    should the Works become suspended for climatic conditions deemed to be
    outside the above description then the Contractor should seek to be paid as
    an Excepted Risk. *clause 20*
(4) Was to ensure the proper execution or safety of the Works; however, whilst
    the proper execution and the safety of the Works is the responsibility of the
    Contractor there may be circumstances which arise in encountering un-
    foreseen physical conditions, delayed commencement due to the Employer
    or such like which necessitate a Suspension whilst the problems are being
    resolved and under these circumstances, any costs arising from such a
    Suspension would be considered to be payable by the Employer.

In order to be paid, it is necessary for the Contractor to give notice of his intention to claim to the Engineer within twenty-eight days of the Engineer's Order and for the Engineer to determine such payments of extra cost and to grant an extension to the Time for Completion as may be appropriate – but it is necessary for the Contractor to give notice of such a claim in writing to the Engineer and not let it pass unregistered.

Having once given a written order to Suspend the Works the Engineer is expected in due course to issue a further order whereby the Works may be recommenced. If he fails to do this within a period of ninety days from the date of Suspension, and unless such a Suspension is given for reasons referred to above, then the Contractor can serve notice upon the Engineer requiring permission to proceed with the Works.

clause 40

If approval to recommence is not given within twenty-eight days from receipt of his request the Contractor, by a further written notice, has the option to treat the Suspension, where it affects only part of the Works, as an omission by Variation under Clause 51, or where it affects the whole of the Works, as being an abandonment of the Contract by the Employer.

If the Contract is abandoned then the Contractor is entitled to be paid in exactly the same manner as if the Contract had been terminated.

clause 65

In general a person seeking payment has to ask for it and these conditions are no exception – this is reasonable because only the Contractor has all the necessary information to hand to do this properly.

Payment – Depending upon the detailed requirements of Part II Clause 60 the Contractor should submit to the Engineer an Application for Payment showing the value of the Permanent and Temporary Works due for payment; this is a task which he willingly undertakes, principally to ensure that there is no delay in the issue of a Certificate of Payment by the Engineer. At the same time it affords him the opportunity of advising the Engineer the precise quantities he considers are correct and of presenting his ideas about the proper levels of new and varied rates. Such a procedure is logical because, notwithstanding the Engineer's obligation to keep progress records of work as performed, it is the Contractor who is obliged to submit a Final Account and he is the one who has invoices, wage sheets, and other records available which are necessary to establish the value of materials on Site and the magnitude of any fluctuations in rates and prices which occur and for which he expects payment. Such an Application for Payment is generally submitted on a monthly basis.

clause 60

In any Application the Contractor should give full details of all claims for additional payments to which he considers himself entitled together with details of all extra or additional work ordered by the Engineer which has been executed during the month covered by the Application.

With this information to hand the Engineer can establish his own assessment of the amount he is prepared to certify to the Employer as being due to the Contractor and such a Certificate of Payment would contain the value of both Permanent and Temporary Works as appropriate, advanced payments for materials on site and other services plus an amount in respect of price fluctuations for labour and material if a price variation clause exists – all of which would be set off as required with the repayment of advances made by the Employer to the Contractor earlier in the Contract. Appropriate deductions for Retention Monies would be made as required by the Conditions of Contract.

clause 60

From the above it can be seen that the Contractor has to provide certain information to enable the Engineer to Certify Payments due to the Contractor. The Employer has to make payment of the amount as Certified within the time specified in the Appendix to the Form of Tender.

Failure by the Employer to make payments to the Contractor which have been certified by the Engineer at the appropriate time can be so damaging to the Contractor that he is given special protection whereby, if not paid the amount due under any Certificate issued by the Engineer within thirty days after such payment has become due, the Contractor is entitled to terminate his employment under the Contract after giving fourteen days prior notice in writing to the

clause 69

Employer, with a copy to the Engineer, following which the Contractor is entitled to remove all of the Constructional Plant then on site.

termination
If termination does occur the Contractor will be paid in accordance with Clause 65 – together with any loss or damage caused to the Contractor consequential upon such termination. *clause 69*

Claims – Within the payment system set out in the FIDIC Conditions many items are paid simply by the application of a unit rate multiplied by the number of quantity units involved. However, many arguments can arise concerning either the application of a rate to the units of work involved or whether such rate should be used at all.

Equally, arguments will arise as to whether certain items of work done are indeed subject to measurement and also if instructions from the Engineer actually vary the Works or if he is merely urging the Contractor to get on with the Works as he should be doing as part of his obligation to complete his Contract.

In seeking to reach an understanding about this particular subject it is common knowledge that more mental gymnastics have been performed by Contractors over the years in order to establish a claim than is possible to guess.
claims
Many Contractors believe that claims provide a panacea by which all their financial troubles can be resolved easily and effectively, even though in many *clause 52* cases the circumstances initiating the recovery of losses by claims are those which have arisen as the result of the Contractor's own shortcomings.

It would also be correct to say that more journalistic endeavours have been devoted to this particular subject than any other and most publications dealing with this matter have been read with avid interest by Contractors – however, claims will always exist and the document permits the Contractor to present any claim he might wish with the knowledge that an obligation is placed upon the Engineer to consider it, however unreal it might be.

Whilst the Engineer's awareness of the Contractor's claim might bring tears to his eyes and sorrow to his heart having read of the Contractor's problem and arguments, he will become extremely hostile if the presentation is unfounded, unsupported and a waste of his time in being obliged to read it – a claim submitted by the Contractor should be cogent, logically argued and well presented and it should be remembered that a claim which is not well presented will command only the minimum of respect which it deserves.

There are certain guidelines to be observed if success is to be achieved, the first being for the Contractor to give proper notice of any claims he intends to make. Details of the claims may be given at time of the notice or later as appropriate. Any claims the Contractor wishes to promote must be made before the issue of the Maintenance Certificate – with the exception possibly of claims arising during the preparation of the Final Account.

The Engineer has a duty to the Employer to accept only those claims which are valid under the Conditions of Contract, and contrary to popular belief, there is no such claim as an "extra-contractual claim" – either the claim exists under the Conditions of Contract or it does not.

The values of the claims made by the Contractor need to be submitted to the Engineer once a month and the claims are required to be given in the fullest of detail as is possible – and whilst the subject of "claims" is mentioned in the clause concerning Variation Orders, the submission of claims is not restricted solely to Variation Order claims as is sometimes argued, but is applicable to the Contract as a whole.

The submission of claims on a monthly basis will be part of the Contractor's Application for Payment and will become part of the value of work performed as and when certified by the Engineer.

Claims are made in all sorts, shapes and sizes and the following list is indicative of the range of items which might form the subject of claims – the list is not intended to cover all possible items.

Disputes over quantities.
Applicability of items in Bills of Quantities.
New items.
Specification interpretation.
Access to Site.
Delay in starting.
Delay during the work.
Disruption.
Awaiting drawings.
Delay in approval by the Engineer or Employer.
Weather conditions.
Method of construction.
Substitution of materials.
Strikes.
Physical conditions.
Difficulty with suppliers.
Alleged defective work.

Actions of a Nominated Sub-Contractor.
Variation orders.
Local customs.
Acceleration.
Suspension.
Exploration.
Action by Employer.
Delay in payment.
Difficulty with Customs.
Work permits.
Tests.
Waivers.
Excepted risks.
Over-abundance of Variation Orders.
Under-utilisation of resources.
Special Risks.

The presentation of a claim can be made in a variety of ways and different Contractors prefer their own form of presentation, but as a suggestion, the following would apply:

(1) Introduction. When presenting a claim it is advisable to give an early summary of the subject-matter being reviewed to save the Engineer and Employer having to read through a number of pages without appreciating the precise purpose of the Document until the very end – it is much better to start with an introduction which gives a brief outline of the Contractor's submission on the first page and develop the claim in detail later.

(2) Historical background. It is helpful in the beginning to give a resumé in as much depth as is necessary of any historical data affecting the subject-matter of the claim and to make the necessary references to other documents which will enable the reader to look up the background of the subject concerned.

(3) Contractual Argument. This is an important part of the presentation in that it should firstly cite the particular clause or clauses upon which the claim is based. Coupled with the naming of the clauses, the Contractor should set out in detail a cogent argument intended to put the Engineer in the same mind as the Contractor about the claim. It may be possible to give references to similar known claims which have been successful in law or arbitration proceedings.

(4) Supporting Data. Matters dealing with this particular part of a Contractor's claim can be recorded under various subject headings and presented as an appendix if desirable. Such data should include, wherever possible, items of the following nature:

Site records.
Photographs.
Diaries.
Charts.
Instructions.
Programmes.

Maps.
Analysis of appropriate unit rates.
Drawings.
Invoices.
Wage sheets.

and any other matters which support the presentation.

(5) Financial. It must be appreciated that there is no set format or standard presentation of financial analysis which will be applicable to each and every claim. The financial presentation must be made to suit the circumstances prevailing but the structure of most financial analysis is basically a comparison between the costs anticipated by the Contractor following the approved programme compared with the costs incurred when actually

doing the Work as affected by the circumstances which gave rise to the claim.

The actual settlement of any claim is a subject which, historically, has become the most negotiable of items within any Final Account. However, if claims are rejected outright or negotiations between the Engineer and the Contractor fail to reach agreement then the disputes arising can follow a predetermined course and become either a "dispute" or "difference" – which, if not resolved by the Engineer following a formal presentation by the Contractor under Clause 67, can be referred to Arbitration.

Execution of Works – During the period of construction it is the Contractor's responsibility to construct the Works and fulfil all his obligations and responsibilities in respect of the suitability of his labour, plant and materials and to ensure that all instructions issued by the Engineer are within the authority given to the Engineer under the terms of the Contract, and also that such instructions are dutifully and expeditiously carried out.

The Contractor is aware that all work which he executes shall be to the satisfaction of the Engineer and that he is required to adhere to such instructions and directions as may be given him – this does not mean that he can seek instructions from the Engineer for solving those problems for which he alone is responsible.

It has happened that when a Contractor was confronted with a problem he has turned to the Engineer for instructions and, upon receipt of what might be termed no better than constructive advice, has sought to change this advice into the status of a Variation Order – this is wrong and Engineers are well aware of such practices – the Contractor must remember that the Engineer is not on Site to perform the Contractor's duties or carry out his obligations or to take away from the Contractor any of his responsibilities or liabilities as defined within the Terms of Contract.

rate of progress – acceleration

Whilst the intended tempo of construction is reflected in the approved programme and in the knowledge that the work must be completed within the Time for Completion, there are occasions when the Contractor might be approached to accelerate his performance and finish earlier. Whilst he might be offered inducements varying from threats to financial awards, he should not forget that the Time for Completion is an agreement existing between himself and the Employer. If it is important for the Employer to have the Works completed earlier then no doubt he and the Contractor will find an arrangement which will satisfy them both and then leave the implementation of the arrangement to the Engineer and the Contractor including the agreement of any revised Value of the Works. *clause 46*

The Contractor has no duty to obey any instruction from the Engineer to accelerate other than in accordance with Clause 46 – rate of progress.

completion of works – time

Time for Completion – At the time the Contractor submitted his Tender he was very conscious of the time available within which he was required to complete the Works and, if failing to do so, to pay Liquidated Damages – always provided, however, that he had not undertaken additional work or had encountered other circumstances which would give him the right for the Time for Completion to be extended. *clause 43*

The Time for Completion is given in the Appendix to the Form of Tender and is required to be given in a number of days – these days will commence the day following the last day of the period named in the Tender within which the Works are required to commence, and will be extended by any such time as shall be determined by the Engineer.

It is noted that the time factor is strictly related to a number of days stated in the Appendix to the Form of Tender and is only related indirectly to the programme which might have been submitted at the Time of Tender or to any other programmes which the Contractor has been obliged to furnish following acceptance of his Tender, but which might show an earlier completion date.

The Time for Completion is fixed and is not subject to adjustment – it is only to be extended as allowed under those clauses which authorise such an extended time to be granted to the Contractor by the Engineer.

Extension of Time – It is the duty of the Engineer to determine the amount of an Extension of Time and he is not bound to take into account any extra or additional works, or indeed the effect of any special circumstances, unless the Contractor has provided the Engineer's Representative with full and detailed particulars of any Extension of Time to which he considers himself entitled – this he must do within twenty-eight days after the additional work has commenced or when any relevant circumstances have arisen, always provided that if it is not done within the twenty eight days but is done as soon as is practicable, this should satisfy the provision of the Clause.

clauses 43, 44

As a matter of general principle, provided the Contractor has followed the procedure of submitting full and detailed particulars of his request for an Extension of Time, it should be granted to him notwithstanding the fact that it might appear that he has no need for such an extension particularly if it is obvious that he would complete the work well within the agreed Time for Completion. Whether he needs it is not the criterion – it is an entitlement to which he has a right if circumstances so dictate.

More particularly is the Contractor conscious of his need for using this entitlement if he is working to a bonus system which would benefit him and is based on a calculation of the differences between the date of the Certificate of Completion and the adjusted Time for Completion as permitted under Clause 44.

clause 47

It should be noted that no mention is made to the effect that omitted work will be taken into account and whilst it is clearly defined in other forms of Contract that the saving of time by omitting work could be offset against the extension of time due to any additional work or circumstances it is not so in the FIDIC Conditions of Contract.

This form of Contract allows only extensions to the Time for Completion and certainly no reduction of time for Variations omitting work is contemplated. It should be borne in mind that, whereas the Engineer may take into account coincidental but different circumstances giving rise to possible extensions to the Time for Completion this form of Contract does not state he should make any allowances for possible reductions.

Completion Certificate – When the Permanent Works for a Section have been completed or when a substantial part of the Permanent Works has been completed to the satisfaction of the Engineer and/or used by the Employer or where the whole of the Works has been substantially completed and satisfactorily passed any Final Tests as may be required, the Contractor may give notice to that effect to the Engineer or his Representative and this is deemed to be a request by him to the Engineer to issue a Certificate of Completion in respect of that Section or the whole of the Works.

clause 48

It should be noted that whilst the Works need not necessarily be totally completed, but only substantially completed, that the Certificate of Completion remains under that name because there is no such thing as a Certificate of Substantial Completion in the FIDIC Conditions of Contract.

The Contractor's request for the issue of a Certificate of Completion should be accompanied by an undertaking from the Contractor to finish off any outstanding Works during the Period of Maintenance. Within twenty-eight days of receiving such request from the Contractor, the Engineer issues to the Contractor (with a copy to the Employer) a Completion Certificate stating the date upon which it is effective, and this indicates that the Work is substantially completed in accordance with the Contract.

If the Engineer declines to issue such a Certificate he is obliged to give instructions in writing to the Contractor specifying all Works which, in his opinion, required to be done before he can issue such a Certificate and he is also obliged to notify the Contractor of any defects in the Work affecting substantial completion that may appear after such instruction and before completion of the Works.

The Contractor is entitled to receive a Certificate of Completion within twenty-one days of Completion to the satisfaction of the Engineer of Works so specified and making good any defects so notified.

clause 48

*certificate –
completion*

The issue of a Certificate of Completion to the Contractor is most important in that it marks the commencements of the Period of Maintenance and also identifies the moment in time when the Contractor ceases to be responsible for the care of the Works and when the Employer takes over that responsibility.

It should be noted that distinctions exist between various Certificates of Completion in that a "Section" of the Permanent Works having an agreed identification can be given a Certificate of Completion in its own right and any "substantial part" of the Permanent Works which has been both completed to the satisfaction of the Engineer and occupied or used by the Employer can be identified as such and it can also be given a Completion Certificate. Furthermore, any part of the Permanent Works which "shall have been substantially completed" to the relevant construction standards and which has passed any Final Test can be the subject of a Certificate of Completion. All these instances of Parts of the Works being covered by a Completion Certificate before completion of the whole of the Works are conditional upon it being understood that the Contractor shall have undertaken to complete all outstanding Works applicable to the appropriate Parts of the Works during the Period of Maintenance.

reinstatement

Finally, there is one exception specified in that, notwithstanding a Certificate of Completion having been given in respect of any Section or part of the Permanent Works before the Completion of the Works as a whole, the issue of the Certificate shall not be deemed to certify completion of ground or other surfaces which require reinstatement – this will apply unless a different understanding is agreed upon, in which case the Certificate of Completion shall state such understanding expressly.

clause 48

*maintenance
period*

Period of Maintenance – Upon being given the Certificate of Completion by the Engineer, applicable to any Section or indeed the whole of the Works, the Contractor then enters into a Period of Maintenance for a predetermined number of weeks or months set out in the Appendix to the Form of Tender.

clause 49

The Engineer has no power to alter or vary the Period of Maintenance either by an Instruction or a Variation Order. None of the agreed outstanding Works carried out during the Period of Maintenance require a separate or new Period of Maintenance. All such Works will be deemed to be completed when the Engineer finally issues the Maintenance Certificate.

repairs

During the Period of Maintenance the Contractor will not only carry out all outstanding Works but will also execute works of repair, amendment, reconstruction, making good defects, imperfections and shrinkages, or indeed making good any other fault which may be required of him by the Engineer – this applies during this period, or within fourteen days following its expiration provided an inspection has been made by the Engineer before the period expires.

Also during this Period of Maintenance the Contractor will keep all Permanent Works in the conditions which were required by the Contract when the Engineer issued a Certificate of Completion, but the Contractor is not responsible for fair wear and tear.

works – damage

In the event of any damage being caused to the Works during this period by the Employer, the repair of such work may be required to be done by the Contractor if so requested by the Engineer – however, it should be noted that during this period the Engineer is not permitted to issue any form of Variation Order because, when he issued a Certificate of Completion, he was then satisfied that no further Variation Orders were necessary for the Works to be considered substantially complete.

clause 49

Any work performed during the Period of Maintenance must be carried out by the Contractor at his own cost if it were the Engineer's opinion that such work was necessary and due to the use of faulty materials or bad workmanship, or if the Contractor has failed to fulfil his obligations. However, if the work is necessary for any other cause it will be paid for by the Employer as if it were additional work – this may necessitate the use of new or adjusted unit rates or for the work to be valued on a daywork basis.

If the Contractor does not perform his obligations during the Period of Maintenance as required by the Engineer, the Employer can engage others to carry out the work and, provided it is the opinion of the Engineer that the Contractor was liable for the costs, then all expenses arising from the Contractor's failure to do the work himself can be deducted from any monies due to him.

3. COMPLETION

Maintenance Certificate – The Maintenance Certificate itself is intended to be issued at approximately the same time as the expiration of the Period of Maintenance but this is not obligatory and it will depend upon the completion of all outstanding work which the Contractor is obliged to perform during the Period of Maintenance.

clauses 61, 62

rtificate –
aintenance

The Engineer is required to issue a Maintenance Certificate as soon as he considers all of the work performed by the Contractor to be to his satisfaction and must be issued by the Engineer without the Contractor being obliged to ask for it.

The Maintenance Certificate is to be given within twenty-eight days following the expiration of the Period of Maintenance provided at that time all Works, including those of a remedial nature, had been completed – if there is still work to be done, then a Maintenance Certificate will not be issued and will remain unissued until such time as the Contractor completes all the outstanding work to the Engineer's satisfaction.

The issuing of a Maintenance Certificate does not terminate those legal responsibilities one Party has with the other – such responsibilities continue for the various times as are prescribed by Law according to their nature. They can be called into account any time within such periods, but can be time-barred if left until the time allowed has expired.

Final Account – During the Period of Construction and certainly during the Period of Maintenance, the Contractor will be working in close conjunction with the Engineer or his Representative to establish a Final Account in a sum they both find acceptable and in so doing should have removed all matters of dispute and disagreement as might have previously existed.

al account

clause 60

The Contract suggests that following the issue of the Maintenance Certificate a period of time be stated in Part II within which the Contractor shall prepare his version of the Final Account and present it to the Engineer. The Engineer is given a stated period after receipt of the Final Account within which he must determine the amount due to the Contractor and issue a Final Certificate.

The Final Certificate is the Engineer's evaluation of the value of the work performed and not that proposed by the Contractor and it should state the amount which, in the Engineer's opinion, is due to the Contractor and show the balance to be paid by the Employer or conversely any amount due to be returned to the Employer as the case may be. Settlement is to be effected within twenty-eight days of the issue of the Final Certificate.

rtificate –
nal account

clause 60

If it is not possible for the Engineer and the Contractor to reach agreement of the value of the Final Account any differences outstanding can be separately identified and referred to Arbitration.

bitration

clause 67

5 ARBITRATION

*arbitration –
disputes*

During the course of the Contract many differences of opinion can occur between the Contractor and the Employer or the Contractor and the Engineer – possibly more of a technical nature during the construction period but towards completion they are more likely to be in respect of the value being placed upon the work performed – this happens because it is only towards the end of the construction period that it is possible to have a reasonably clear indication of the probable value of the Final Account and it is then when differences of a financial nature *clause 67* take on a more important status.

Because differences of a technical and financial nature can and do arise there exists within the Contract the facility for referring those differences which cannot be resolved to an independent authority who will decide objectively who is right and who is wrong and how and when any award will be implemented – this is by Arbitration.

The differences or disputes once identified need not wait until the Works have been completed but can be referred to Arbitration at any time provided always that both Parties realise that their responsibilities and obligations under the Terms of the Contract are in no way altered.

The right of the Parties to refer disputes to Arbitration is already predetermined by the Conditions of Contract to be under the International Chamber of Commerce Rules of Conciliation and Arbitration. Settlement of the dispute will be by one or more Arbitrators appointed in accordance with such rules and who will have all powers possible to open up and revise any decision, opinion, direction or valuation of the Engineer. Neither party is limited in any way to placing evidence or arguments before the Arbitrators to matters of evidence already put before the Engineer for the purpose of obtaining his decision.

The International Chamber of Commerce will be acting under its own particular rules and procedures but it is important to recognise that unless these rules conform to the statutes or legislation operative within the country wherein the Works are being constructed and not the venue of the Arbitration – then the laws of the country will always take precedence. This is understandable because if an Arbitration award is to have the legal support of the country in which the Works are being constructed, then, unless these Arbitration procedures conform to these laws and requirements, any award made might not be enforceable in that country.

Reference of a dispute to Arbitration is a major decision because it will entail considerable costs in time and money which might never be recovered. It is because of this the International Chamber of Commerce is willing to act as a "conciliator", if requested so to do by the Parties in dispute and resolve the dispute before embarking upon full Arbitration proceedings.

Prior to Arbitration, both Parties will have obtained legal guidance about the laws applicable to the subject in the country concerned – these laws might well affect the selection of the nationality of the Arbitrators and venue where such proceedings are to take place and whether the award made by the Arbitrator can be challenged and overturned or if such an award is considered sacrosanct and must remain as given.

When both Parties reach the stage of entering into Arbitration, they have generally consulted legal advisors of considerable eminence and no doubt have both been assured that victory is theirs, and that there is only little or no doubt that each will win. Any Party who is assured of a positive victory in advance of the award, nevertheless, should apply commercial expertise and judgement to evaluate the position should he surprisingly become the eventual loser and not the winner.

Before a dispute is referred to Arbitration there are certain procedures which need to be observed and these are primarily that the Contractor or the Employer should refer to the Engineer any dispute or difference in such specific terms under Clause 67 to enable the Engineer to give a positive and unequivocal decision and once he has made this decision it is his duty to communicate it both to the Employer and the Contractor alike.

This decision-making by the Engineer shall be done within a period of ninety days after being requested to do so by either the Employer or the Contractor and any decision made is to be considered as final and binding upon both Parties and be given immediate effect.

Having once given written notice of his decision the Engineer does nothing further. Within the following ninety days from the date of his decision, either the Employer or the Contractor may communicate with him expressing dissatisfaction with his decision and giving notice of the intention to refer the dispute to Arbitration. If, however, the ninety days passes without such notice being given by either Party then the decision will remain final and binding and the Contractor and the Employer must abide by the decision.

Should the Engineer not give a decision within the ninety days after being requested to do so, or if either the Employer or the Contractor notify dissatisfaction with any decision given within the ninety days, they are both permitted within ninety days after the date when the Engineer should have given the decision or ninety days after a decision has been given and with which they are not satisfied to refer the dispute to Arbitration.

Despite his previous involvement as a decision-maker the Engineer under Clause 67 of the Contract is not precluded from being called as a witness and giving evidence to the Arbitrator. During the interim period Arbitration proceedings are continuing the Engineer is not precluded from conducting a dialogue with the Contractor to seek a solution to the dispute – but he would have no authority actually to settle it.

The Rules and Procedures of the International Chamber of Commerce are readily available from the headquarters in Paris and probably offer the most economical and expeditious manner by which disputes can be resolved together with a high degree of confidentiality because the actions are not held in open court. The International Chamber of Commerce can recommend on request experienced and available Arbitrators on most subjects, which will enable an award to be made expeditiously and within a specified period.

It should be noted by the reader that, notwithstanding Clause 67 requiring disputes to be settled under the Rules of Conciliation and Arbitration of the International Chamber of Commerce in Paris, it could well be agreed between both parties at the time of formulation of the Contract that disputes might be settled equally conveniently under the Rules of some other recognised authority such as the London Court of Arbitration at the International Arbitration centre in London.

6 MISCELLANY

In an analysis of a Contract Document such as this there are a number of clauses which can be dealt with more objectively in general terms rather than grouping them with other clauses.

In considering the remaining matters of interest it will be seen that most are by nature concerned with procedure or clarification rather than with responsibilities and obligations – nevertheless, they must be studied as they are of particular importance when seeking to understand the Document as a whole.

definitions
In the same manner as anyone wishing to read and understand a map has his attention directed towards the legend which gives the meaning of the various signs and symbols which have been used, so have those studying the Conditions of Contract been directed to providing definitions and interpretations of expressions used in the Documents – in fact this clause is of the greatest importance to *clause 1* the reader of the Document because it is necessary to understand the various expressions used and to identify clearly their respective meanings and limitations.

singular/plural
Whilst the distinction that singular will also include the plural and vice-versa might at first sight seem valueless – on reflection it can be understood that it is essential to clarify this point to obviate argument.

cost
It is helpful to know that the word "cost" will include overhead costs whether on or off the Site but it is difficult to understand why there should be an exclusion of a profit margin on "costs" other than in particularly specified cir- *clause 1* cumstances.

assigning
The Contractor is not permitted to assign the Contract or any part thereof or to enter into agreements where any benefits or interests arise without the prior written consent of the Employer – but this will exclude any arrangement which *clause 3* the Contractor has with his Bankers in respect of overdrafts and loans.

sub-letting
Notwithstanding the fact that the Contractor is responsible for the proper and expeditious execution of the Works he is not allowed to sub-let the whole of the Works – unless already agreed within the Contract – nor will he sub-let any *clause 4* part of the Works without the prior written consent of the Engineer being given, but this should not be unreasonably withheld.

Once such consent is given it does not relieve the Contractor of any of his liabilities or obligations under the Contract and under such an arrangement he will remain responsible for all acts, defaults and neglects of such Sub-Contractors and will be fully responsible for their performance and conduct in exactly the same manner as he is for his own organisation.

The sub-letting of work would exclude the provision of labour on a piece-work basis as this is deemed to be work performed by the Contractor himself.

documents –
status
It is obviously desirable for a status or precedence to be established for the various Documents of which the Contract is composed and this is done in recognising that the Provisions of the Conditions of Contract Part I and Part II shall prevail over all other documents.

ambiguities
In recognising that several documents will form the Contract as a whole these are expected to be mutually explanatory each to the other but it is understood that, as and when instances of ambiguities or discrepancy occur, these will be referred to the Engineer who will explain the intention and make such adjust- *clause 5* ments as are necessary, and will issue the Contractor with instructions. If it is the opinion of the Engineer that his instructions to the Contractor will involve the

Contractor in any additional costs which otherwise would not have arisen then he will certify such costs for payment.

It is necessary for the proper execution of the Works for the Contractor to provide superintendence and to exercise control by employing a competent and authorised Agent or Representative who must be approved by the Engineer – such approval will be given in writing but it may be withdrawn without any reason being given. The authorised Agent is to attend constantly at the Site of the Works and is required to devote his whole time to his duties. It is current practice in the construction industry to use the style "Project Manager" for "Agent". *clause 15*

Contractor – agent

It the Engineer decides to withdraw his approval, the Contractor, as soon as practicable, will remove the Agent from the Works and no longer employ him in any capacity but shall replace him by another Agent whose appointment likewise will need the Engineer's approval.

The Contractor's Agent will receive directions and instructions from the Engineer and, within the limitation of the Engineer's delegation of authority, any instructions or directions which are given to the Contractor by the Engineer's Representative.

The Contractor must be particularly selective in the appointment of his Agent as he will be relying upon him to exercise judgements and skills and to make decisions often without reference to his Head Office. In the event of the Agent not performing efficiently and making mistakes it is not possible for the Contractor to use an error by the Agent to escape any of his responsibilities.

Contractors – staff

It is in the Contractor's interests as well as that of the Employer to ensure that the Contractor only employs technical assistants who are skilled in their respective callings and are competent to give proper supervision to the work in which they are involved. The numbers of skilled, semi-skilled and unskilled labour should be limited to those necessary for the proper and timely execution and maintenance of the Works. *clause 16*

If the Engineer objects to any person employed by the Contractor who, in the opinion of the Engineer, misconducts himself or is incompetent or negligent in the proper execution of his duties, or for that matter should it just be considered undesirable that his employment will continue, then such a person will not again be employed upon the Works without the written permission of the Engineer. The removal of any of the Contractor's employees is an obligation which the Contractor must undertake when instructed by the Engineer but such an instruction does not allow the Contractor to claim for any costs involved.

From the above it can be seen that whereas the Contractor's Agent, if dismissed from Site, will never return – insofar as technical assistants and other skilled, semi-skilled and unskilled labour are concerned, if these are removed and if the Engineer relents or changes his opinion later, then such people can be re-employed upon the Works, provided the Engineer gives permission in writing.

Setting out

The setting out of any major Works is partly done by the Engineer and partly by the Contractor and if any errors arise in the setting out of the Works, because the original references given by the Engineer were at fault, then the Contractor will be compensated. *clause 17*

The Contractor has the duty of ensuring the correct setting out of the Works from the references given to him by the Engineer and in so doing will carefully protect and preserve all bench-marks, survey stations and other marks which are required for this purpose. He is not expected to set out the entire project himself as the main datum points and grid formations are the responsibility of the Engineer.

Instruments

The Contractor must provide all necessary instruments, appliances and labour in connection with the setting out and this can be an extremely costly operation depending upon the requirements of the Engineer. It is prudent to seek clarification at the time of Tender about the extent of this commitment as it would not be unexpected for the Contractor to be asked to provide the permanent use of a vehicle and linesmen – all to be placed at the disposal of the Engineer or his Representatives either because they are "necessary" and because the vehicles are "appliances". A list of items and commitments under this clause should be provided in the Specification or Instructions to Tenderers.

bore holes

If at any time during the execution of the Works the Contractor is required to drill bore holes or make exploratory excavations then such work will be done under the instruction of the Engineer and will constitute a Variation Order, unless of course a Provisional Sum has been included in the Bills of Quantities.   *clause 18*

It will not have escaped notice that bore holes and exploratory excavations are only possible during the "execution of the Works" by dealing with them as a Variation under Clause 51 and this would mean that the Engineer can only use this clause up to the time he issues a Completion Certificate.

In the event of any bore holes or exploratory excavation being required in searching for defects during the Maintenance Period this clause is not applicable and the work should be dealt with under Clause 50.   *clause 50*

security

It is the Contractor's responsibility to provide and maintain at his own costs all necessary lights, guards, fencing and watching which are necessary or indeed are required by the Engineer or his Representative – likewise should any constituted authority require similar provisions for the protection of the Works or the safety or convenience of the public then these will be supplied. It is noted that this is an obligation placed upon the Contractor but if there be an item applicable to be found within the Bills of Quantities then he will be paid – but if not then this will be done at his own cost because it is one of his obligations under the Contract and the cost thereof is deemed to be included as an element elsewhere provided within the rates and prices of the Bills of Quantities.   *clause 19*

notices

During the Period of Construction there are generally notices to be given to various authorities and fees to be paid and it is the responsibility of the Contractor to attend to such matters.   *clause 26*

fees

Any monies paid by the Contractor in connection with these notices and fees will be repaid to him and the Engineer will certify the amounts in the normal manner.

site ownership

The Contract recognises that the Employer and the Contractor could, under certain circumstances, be regarded as one in matters of law – for example, they are both involved in the occupation of a particular area of land – one as the owner and the other as an occupier – and work done on this land could not only affect public utilities and such-like already in being but also the public at large should they have access to use the land either by custom or statute. The Contract, however, makes the Contractor responsible for conforming in all respects with any statute, ordinance or law and all regulations and bye-laws seemingly from whatever origin and he will keep the Employer indemnified against all penalties and liabilities of whatever kind should such laws be broken – but obviously if the law is broken by the Employer himself the Contractor would be indemnified.   *clause 42*

statutes regulations

  clause 26

antiquities

During the course of construction excavation will often disclose items of antiquity such as coins and fossils and items of geological or archaeological interest. If this should happen the finder does not become the owner because all such discoveries can become the property of the Employer. Whilst this is so for the purpose of the Contract the Employer himself might not be the legal owner if his Enterprise is being constructed on land which he does not own – then the owner of the land would no doubt claim possession.   *clause 27*

Because of the importance of such discoveries the Contractor must take all reasonable precautions to prevent his own work-people or others from removing or damaging such discoveries and immediately they are found will acquaint the Engineer's Representative with what has been found and he will receive instructions about the preservation or disposal of the discoveries. Work so undertaken will be at the expense of the Employer. Any events of this nature might qualify for an extension to the Time for Completion.

patents

Because different types of construction require different techniques involving specialist construction equipment there is always a possibility that patent rights could be infringed and proceedings instigated. In this matter the Contractor must indemnify the Employer completely from claims and legal actions arising from such matters and will bear all damages and costs of whatever nature if involved in settling any claim.   *clause 28*

This Clause also recognises the need for the Contractor to obtain and use

natural resources

stone, sand, gravel, clay or other natural materials which are required for the construction of the Works but it places upon him the obligation to pay for the supply of all such materials and also the royalties which might be involved together with rents and other payments if these arise when obtaining such materials.

There are obviously a number of situations which can arise in the purchasing and obtaining of such materials – the most general form is direct purchase from a supplier. However, there can be alternative situations where the Contractor can himself, by arrangement with a local landowner, become the quarrymaster and if this was his intention he should have made it known to the Employer at the time of Tender in order that a fair and comparable basic price for the supply of such material could be established at the time of Tender and used as and when appropriate for calculating any variation in price for the supply of such materials.

There can also be circumstances when the Employer himself becomes involved in the supplying of materials and this could mean the materials being on a free issue to the Contractor, or the Employer can sell any such material to the Contractor in the same manner as if he were an ordinary supplier. In both of these situations the Contractor is advised to understand his liability in the event that the material supplied by the Employer should prove defective.

materials defective

Whilst it would be possible for the Contractor to sue a normal supplier in respect of defective materials it becomes a complicated situation where the Employer is the Supplier. Obviously when the material is given freely to the Contractor it might be claimed that the Employer incurs no liability in that no Contract of Sale exists between them. But when the Employer provides such material and is paid for it by the Contractor then his position becomes changed in that he is then in a Contract of Sale with the Contractor and as such should carry any liabilities for defective material. He would be in an even more unusual position, not only being a Supplier but also retaining his title as the Employer with all his liabilities. An even more confusing situation exists if he has already qualified the documents by stating the materials he supplies are the only materials which the Engineer will approve.

clause 39

From the above it can be seen that it is important for the Contractor clearly to define his position at the time of Tender in respect of any materials supplied by the Employer and particularly as to the Employer's liability in the event of materials proving defective.

traffic

In order that the Works can be constructed and maintained, it is necessary for traffic of many kinds to use the public and private roads for access and it is the Contractor's responsibility to ensure as far as possible that he does not interfere unnecessarily or improperly with the convenience of the public. He must also make certain that no inconvenience is caused to the owners of private roadways, footpaths or properties irrespective of whether they are in the possession of the Employer or anyone else.

clause 29

In the event of any expense, damages or such-like, arising from the Contractor's failure properly to comply with the requirements as set out, then he will be fully responsible for the costs arising – obviously if the Employer caused damages when supplying items of plant or such-like, then these costs will be borne by him and not the Contractor.

traffic – extraordinary

One of the difficulties concerned with the movement of heavy vehicles is the need to use highways or to cross bridges which, by their age or the condition of their structure, could be damaged. If such damage is a possibility the Contractor is required to select routes, choose appropriate vehicles and restrict and distribute such loads in such a way, and as far as reasonably possible, to ensure that no unnecessary damage or injury occurs to any highways or bridges.

clause 30

special loads

There will be circumstances when the use of highways or bridges becomes essential for heavy vehicles and no alternative is possible and damage to them is probable. When this situation is likely to occur the Contractor should give notice to the Engineer or his Representative of the weight and other particulars of the load to be moved, together with his proposals for protecting or strengthening the highway or bridge which might suffer.

Unless within the fourteen days following receipt of such notice the Engineer states that such protection or strengthening is unnecessary the Contractor will get on with the work he proposed and will incorporate any modification which the Engineer requires. If there are items in the Bills of Quantities for pricing this work then the Contractor will be paid according to these items but if no such items exist then the costs which are incurred will be paid by the Employer to the Contractor. *clause 30*

If having followed the required procedure the Contractor does actual damage or causes injury to highways or bridges because of the movement of heavy vehicles and receives a claim arising therefrom the Employer, and not the Contractor, will negotiate and settle all sums due in respect of such claims and shall indemnify the Contractor accordingly. Provided always that if the Engineer is of the opinion that any damage, which has arisen and for which the Employer has settled the claim, is due to any failure on the part of the Contractor to observe and perform his obligations to select an appropriate route or to strengthen any highway or bridge the Contractor will be deemed to have been responsible and claims which have been paid by the Employer will be repaid to the Employer.

In general terms this means that it is the Contractor's responsibility to use the highways and bridges without changing them, but if they need strengthening and the Engineer agrees, the Employer will pay the costs involved – but if the Contractor does not involve the Employer then he will pay the costs himself.

traffic – water-borne Where waterborne traffic is involved the canal or waterway is to be regarded as a highway which will include sea walls, locks, docks or other structures as related to a waterway. Water craft and such-like are to be treated in the same manner as vehicular traffic. *clause 30*

clearance of site The Contractor is obliged to keep the Site reasonably free from unnecessary obstructions and to store or dispose of any Constructional Plant or surplus materials as appropriate and will finally clear away and remove from the Site all wreckage, rubbish or Temporary Works when no longer required. *clause 32*

It is more than possible during the progress of the Works that the Engineer will have reason to complain to the Contractor that he is not fulfilling this obligation as often as is desirable and will issue instructions to the Contractor to perform this particular duty in a more frequent and workmanlike manner – such an instruction is not a Variation Order as it is already an obligation of the Contractor – only if the frequency is more than required in the Specification could it become an Order.

completion – clear away On the completion of the Works, the Contractor will clear away and remove from the Site everything which he has provided for the purpose of Construction and leave the whole of the Site and Works clean and in a workmanlike condition to the satisfaction of the Engineer – and should this requirement become one of the items which the Engineer accepts as being done under the Maintenance Period then until it is finally carried out to his satisfaction he will not issue the Maintenance Certificate. *clause 33*

On major Works there are possibly a number of contractors operating simultaneously for the same Employer on the same Site. Each contractor is required to afford all reasonable opportunities to other contractors carrying out their work either on Site or near the Site of any work included in the Scope of Works of the *other contractors* first contractor – this places any contractor in a very difficult situation when other contractors experience strikes or lock-outs and may make it impossible for the first contractor to proceed with his own work. Under these circumstances the contractor could claim for an Extension of Time but would find it extremely difficult *clause 31* to obtain financial compensation unless he has qualified his Tender and had it accepted that he will recover all costs so incurred by the effect of strikes if the trouble is not domestic to his own company.

If required by the Engineer, the Contractor is obliged to deliver to the Engineer's Representative a return showing in detail and in such a manner as the Engineer may prescribe records of numbers of the various classes of labour *returns – labour* employed by the Contractor. This return must be provided at intervals to suit the *clause 35* Engineer and, if required, similar information is to be given about the Constructional Plant and such-like on Site.

The Contractor should be aware that this information is extremely useful to the Engineer in checking any claim from the Contractor which seeks payment under the Conditions of the Contract; more particularly if the information is detailed in such a way as to show to the Engineer the specific activities upon which the labour force were engaged.

Conversely, this is equally helpful to the Contractor when making a claim because information about the resources of plant and labour which have not been fully utilised is thereby already in the hands of the Engineer and, because it can be verified at the appropriate time, it will ensure that as little argument as possible will arise about the facts concerning the cost element of the Contractor's claim.

materials –
quality

clause 36

The Specification gives details of standards of materials and of workmanship required for the Works and will be in accordance with any instruction the Engineer might issue. The standards achieved should not be necessarily better and certainly not lower than those specified. The Engineer may have materials or equipment tested either at the place of manufacture or on site or elsewhere in order to be satisfied that they are of the adequate quality.

The Contractor is obliged to provide such assistance, instruments, machines, labour and materials as are normally required in the examination, measurement and testing of any work and is also obliged to supply such samples of materials before incorporation in the Works as the Engineer requires for test purposes. All samples supplied by the Contractor will be at his own expense if already clearly intended as such in the Contract. If the samples are not already part of the Contract then the Employer must pay the cost.

samples

testing

The cost of testing will be borne by the Contractor if it is clearly intended to be within the Contract but if a test is ordered by the Engineer which has never been intended or not provided for in the Specification, then the cost of such tests will be borne by the Contractor only if the results show that the workmanship or materials are not in accordance with the provisions of the Contract. If the tests are successful then the costs will be borne by the Employer.

The need for testing will sometimes be required simply because the finished work does not appear to be up to the standard required by the Specification, and the Engineer is completely within his rights in not accepting such Works until he is completely satisfied. However, there can be times when a doubt exists as to the exact cause of apparent imperfections and, under such circumstances, testing is a method of determining such cause of imperfection for the benefit of the Engineer and the Contractor alike.

If the Contractor is completely satisfied that the materials and workmanship which were used conformed entirely with the requirements of the Specification then it is in his own interest to examine the problem with more than average concern and, if necessary, seek specialist assistance to establish the cause of apparent imperfections.

For example, a large steel bridge was required to be painted with a combination of various metallic-based paints but during the Period of Maintenance it was seen that the paintwork has started to break down, to discolour and to foam.

Because of its appearance the Engineer condemned the work as being unacceptable, classified it as defective work and ordered the paint to be renewed and the steel bridge repainted. The Contractor, however, was satisfied that no fault could be found in the material used or in the manner of application which would justify his being held responsible.

The Contractor then took samples and these, together with the Specification, were referred to expert analysis whereupon it was discovered that, whilst the Specification was without fault in general terms, the paint was nevertheless completely inappropriate for use on this Site. This was because the bridge was located in a large industrial area with an extremely high level of sulphur pollution and when it rained, it generated a galvanic electrical discharge sufficient to cause the paint to foam and be unacceptable. The fault was identified as one of design and not one of defective materials and workmanship. The Contractor did not claim this situation to be covered by Clause 12 because a Certificate of Completion under Clause 44 had already been issued and therefore it was accepted as a matter of design rather than an unforeseen physical condition and hence covered as an Excepted Risk.

The example is given only to demonstrate the need for further investigations when confronted with an apparently inexplicable occurrence of defective work. In the above case the Contractor was not paid for his Tests as these were not instructed by the Engineer but he was paid for repainting as necessary.

It is important for the Engineer to have authority to enable him, or any person authorised by him, to have access to the work and all workshops and places where work is being prepared or from where manufactured articles or *access* machinery are being obtained for the Works.   *clauses 11, 37*

The Contractor is only obliged to afford every facility and assistance for obtaining the right for such access but beyond that he has no obligation.

Particularly with matters of excavation there is a need for parts of the foundation, structure and other items of work to be examined and approved by the Engineer or his Representative and it is important that the Contractor ensures that no work is covered up or put out of sight without the approval of the Engin- *covering up* eer. He must give notice to the Engineer's Representative when any work or foundations are ready for examination before being covered up. The Engineer's Representative is obliged to act without unreasonable delay if he wishes to attend   *clause 38* for the purpose of examining or measuring the work but if he considers it not necessary to be present, he should advise the Contractor accordingly.

There will be circumstances when the Engineer will require certain works which have been covered up to be uncovered. If this is necessary the Contractor will uncover those parts of the work as may be required by the Engineer and, if these are found to have been executed in accordance with the Contract, then the expense incurred will be borne by the Employer. But if the work when exposed is unsatisfactory then the costs of exposing the work and of making good such work will be borne by the Contractor.

It has already been recognised that the Contractor is responsible for the *workmanship –* proper execution of the Works together with ensuring that the standards of ma-
quality of terials and workmanship conform to the Specification. If, however, during the progress of the Works failure to observe the proper standards can be seen the Con-   *clause 36* tractor should immediately correct this situation himself without waiting to be told. But there are times when other matters are given greater priority and such work of correction remains undone.

If this happens the Engineer is empowered to issue the Contractor with an *materials – con-* order in writing to remove from the Site any materials which, in the opinion of the
demned Engineer, are not in accordance with the Contract.   *clause 39*

He can also require the substitution of proper and suitable materials as well as the removal and re-execution of any work which in his opinion is not in accordance with the Contract. He can do this even if previous tests have not detected the imperfections or indeed if interim payment has already been made.

Should the Contractor fail to carry out such a written order from the Engineer, the Employer is entitled to bring other people on Site to carry out the Engineer's instructions and all expenses consequential or incidental thereto shall be paid by the Contractor and such expenses may be deducted by the Employer from any amounts certified by the Engineer which may be due to the Contractor for carrying out the work.

Occasionally with some Enterprises the Contractor requires to obtain temporary wayleaves whereby he can obtain suitable and proper access to the Site; also he might require additional accommodation outside the Site for the purpose of executing the Works. If the temporary wayleaves or additional accommoda- *wayleaves* tion are, in fact, provided by the Employer, outside the boundaries of the area   *clause 42* within which the Works are being constructed, then such wayleaves and additional accommodation may be classified by the Contract as being the Site – but *accommodation* where this is not so, then the Contractor is obliged to bear all the costs and charges for special or temporary wayleaves or any additional accommodation. Separate arrangements between the Contractor and the various landowners involved will be made, and it will be for the Contractor, at his own cost, to restore *landowner* any land so used back to its original condition or to pay compensation in lieu.

Before the Certificate of Completion is issued or during the Period of Maintenance the Contractor can be given notice by the Engineer in writing to search for the cause of any defect or imperfection which appears – this is done at the direction of the Engineer and if the defects or imperfections should prove to be for *Contractor to* any reason the responsibility of the Contractor then the cost involved in searching *search – defects* and for the repairing or rectification is borne by the Contractor. However, if it *clause 50* proves that it is a defect or imperfection for which the Contractor is not liable then the cost of the search will be borne by the Employer as will be the cost of repair, rectification and making good as may be necessary and instructed by the Engineer.

It can sometimes happen during the period of constructing the Works or during the Period of Maintenance that an accident or failure or some other event will occur in connection with the Works which requires remedial work to be done *Repairs – urgent* as a matter of urgency to ensure the safety of the Works. The Contractor will be *clause 64* asked to undertake this work but, should he be unable or unwilling to do so immediately, then the Employer may employ others to carry out such works as the Engineer or his Representative may consider necessary. If this work, in the opinion of the Engineer, was a liability of the Contractor then all expenses incurred by the Employer in arranging for it to be done by others will be recovered from the Contractor by the Employer.

There is always the proviso that if the Engineer or the Engineer's Representative does not notify the Contractor in writing as soon after the occurrence of any such emergency as may be reasonably practicable, and thereby afford the Contractor the opportunity of doing the work himself, then such costs of remedial work or repair will be borne by the Employer.

During the course of the Contract there are many certificates, notices and written orders which can be given by the Engineer or the Employer to the Contractor under the terms of the Contract and these must be properly served by *Addresses* sending by post or delivering to the Contractor's principal place of business or any other addresses that the Contractor shall nominate. It is not sufficient to give such notices to the Contractor's Agent on Site although it is common practice for *clause 68* Certificates of Payment to be passed to him direct to avoid unnecessary delay in transit.

Likewise, when the Contractor is obliged under similar circumstances to give notices to either the Engineer or the Employer under the Terms of the Contract these will be sent by post or delivered to the respective addresses which have been given.

Addresses – Either Party may find the need to change the nominated address to another *change of* in the country where the work is being executed and this is done by giving prior notice. Obviously should the Engineer require to do the same then he is obliged to give written notice to both Parties.

It is a rare contract in this age where no adjustment to the Contract Price needs to be made in respect of a rise or fall in the cost of labour or materials or *Increase/* other matters which affect the cost of executing the Works. Details of such adjust- *clause 70* *Decrease in costs* ments and their base points of calculation should be given in the Specification or the Instructions to Tenderers or given in particular detail under this clause within Part II.

Obviously, the manner of adjustment will vary according to the definitions within the Contract and whilst this might vary from a simple formula applied to the value of work done to the more expensive and once traditional method of directly relating wage sheets and invoices to basic prices it should be remembered that once the method of adjusting the Contract Price is agreed then this is part of the Contract and cannot be changed either by the Engineer or the Contractor without the approval of both Parties to the Contract.

At the time of tendering the Contractor will have paid particular attention to the laws of the country and have become aware of the effect of statutes, ordin- *Law – changes of* ances, regulations or bye-laws and other such regulations and will have based his *clause 70* Tender on such knowledge. In the event of changes to the statutes, laws, decrees and ordinances, as occurring within thirty days of the latest date for submission of Tenders, then if the effect of these changes is to increase or decrease the costs to the Contractor for executing the Works such additional or decreased costs are to be certified by the Engineer and the Contract Price adjusted accordingly.

currencies

In preparing his Tender the Contractor will be using currencies which are not always the same as his own and will be aware that the build-up of his Tender Prices is required to be based upon the rates of exchange existing thirty days prior to the last date before the submission of Tenders. In the event that after the date upon which the rates are based the country in which the works are being executed imposes currency restrictions, or restrictions on the transfer of currency, the Employer will reimburse any loss or damage to the Contractor resulting there-from.

clause 71

Whilst the Contractor could have maintained a reasonable control of his financial destiny during the Works by being both competent in performance and efficient in Tendering a situation can arise which is almost completely outside his control when it comes to the timing of receiving payments. This is when he is involved in a fortuitious or disadvantageous position because of a change in rates of exchange.

rates of exchange

The Contract legislates that, where it provides for payment in whole or in part in foreign currencies, then such payment shall not be subject to variation in rates of exchange between the currencies of the country where the Works are being performed and the foreign currency required. This means that where items have been priced for example in US dollars, then the Contractor will receive pre-cisely that number of dollars as payment and this will not be changed in number simply because the rates of exchange when related to the currency of the country in which the works are to be executed have altered in respect of the US dollar.

clause 72

However, where the Employer has required the Tender to be expressed in a single currency but where it had been agreed that this calculated value was to be paid in different currencies then, provided the Contractor has already stated the proportions or amounts of such other currencies in which he required payment to be made, the rates of exchange applicable to calculating the payment of such pro-portions or amounts shall be fixed as those given by the Central Bank of the country in which the Works are being executed on the date thirty days before the last date of the submission of Tender. This will have been notified by the Employ-er to the Contractor before the Tender was submitted or else would have been provided for as such in the Tender Documents.

Where the Contract provides for payment in more than one currency, and Provisional Sums are involved, the amounts to be paid in respect of currencies for such Provisional Sums shall be as set out, unless of course, the Nominated Sub-Contractors involved with any Provisional Sum have already stipulated their own requirements insofar as currency is concerned and this has been accepted by the Employer when the Engineer instructed the Main Contractor to place an order with the Nominated Sub-Contractor.

taxation

The particular status of any Enterprise might give it a privileged position in respect of taxation matters which affect the Contractor and his personnel, and it is therefore of importance to the Contractor to examine the taxation position in as much detail as possible. He should know whether his employees are exempt or otherwise in any way from local income tax or other forms of taxes. He will examine his own position as a Company by finding out whether the Company can enjoy any relief from taxation extended by a Government to those involved in the construction of the Works in its country.

clause 73

It is an important obligation placed on the Contractor in many countries that he will conform with all Government regulations and in particular he should be concerned with those which impose a strong discipline over the use of explos-ives, bribes and corruption, taking of photographs of the Works, advertising, non-disclosure of secret information, submission of shipping and other docu-ments and the like, and indeed all of those matters which might affect the security of the country in which he is working. He should give particular attention to the strict observance of religious laws and those obligations which might affect his

regulations by
government

work-people and reflect all of these matters within the Tender Price. Observance
of such regulations and laws does not attract additional payment, and only in
special circumstances will it entitle him to an extension of Time for Completion.   *clause 74*

7 SELECTED COMMENTARY

Hitherto, except for referring to the FIDIC Conditions in general terms in 1 – THE CONTRACT and in 6 – MISCELLANY, the text of this book has concerned itself with the Parties to the Contract and to others who are intimately involved in the design and execution of the Works of the Enterprise.

In this new section commentary is made on a number of selected clauses from Part I – GENERAL CONDITIONS – to examine their imperfections and to offer suggestions for improving them based on experience at large and on the views of those readers of the first edition who have contacted us.

Nevertheless, as is well known in the world of construction, people produce the works of civil engineering construction – and indeed most other forms of creation – often in spite of the many words which are written to discipline their activities and to help them to conduct themselves in a rational and business-like manner each to the other.

Therefore a strong appeal must be made to all concerned in the construction industry that they should unite to achieve the ultimate goal – the design and construction of the Enterprise to be on time and within the budget cost simultaneously bearing in mind the economics of the operational and maintenance costs of the Enterprise, which are of particular importance to the user.

DEFINITIONS AND INTERPRETATION

site

clause 1 (m)

It is noted that the "Site" is defined as the place where the Permanent Works and the Temporary Works are to be executed together with other places which the Employer provides as working space in order to enable the Works to be executed.

To be given a precisely defined area when tendering is also of financial importance in that it determines the applicability or otherwise of ownership of and payment for materials delivered to the Site and also of the complicated provisions involving insurance.

Although it might be convenient for the Contractor or, for that matter, the Engineer to have temporary offices and other buildings on the Site as defined, it should be borne in mind that, in general, all Works on Site tend to become the property of the Employer. There could be occasions when the provision of offices and the like off site are advantageous to the Contractor and the Engineer because these offices and other buildings can be sold at the end of the Contract or used for other activities which in themselves are not connected with the Contract itself.

It would seem appropriate that the "Site" should also embody places nominated by the Contractor for undertaking any Temporary Works. It is suggested that Contract Drawing No. 1 should be provided as an important part of the Contract Documents to show precisely the boundaries of those areas of land referred to in the definition of the Site.

It would be suitable also to show on this Contract Drawing No. 1 the means of access to the Site and in particular where the Employer himself makes arrangement for a wayleave or where such access is provided by him.

access to site

Furthermore it should be obligatory for the Employer to obtain as part of the Contract any special or temporary wayleaves as are necessary to provide access to the Site to the extent required by the Contractor. This seems logical in that the Employer, whilst investigating the feasibility of his Enterprise, would have been in contact with other landowners over whose land he would require access.

Engineer

clause 1(1) (c)

In considering the definition of the "Engineer" it can be seen that the Employer can appoint other Engineers during the life time of the Contract. Any change of the Engineer will inevitably bring about problems for both the Employer and the Contractor but it would appear reasonable that the Employer should seek prior agreement with the Contractor before the appointment of a new Engineer.

The reason for this arrangement is that when the Contractor submits a tender in the knowledge that a particular Engineer has been appointed for the Enterprise it can often govern his price and performance – it is not unknown amongst contractors that certain tenders become unattractive if performed under the disciplines imposed by different Engineers. The tender price might be increased if the Contractor felt the disciplines under which he would operate under a particular Engineer were much more onerous than those applied by a different Engineer.

Cost

clause 1(4)

This clause has raised comment in seeking to establish precisely what is intended to be paid to the Contractor.

It is reasoned that if the Contractor is required to perform any Work where there is an obligation for the Employer to pay then such Work would warrant the payment of an element of profit, therefore a more appropriate wording of this clause should be:

"the word cost shall be deemed to include overhead costs of whatever nature whether on or off the site and to include a reasonable element of profit".

Scope of works

new sub-clause 1(5)

It has been customary for a description of the Scope of Works to be given within the Specification or some other Contract Document. Although this is not obligatory nevertheless to have a contractual definition of the nature and extent of the Works being undertaken would place the contract on a much firmer foundation than at present. Therefore it is recommended that a sub-clause should be inserted in Clause 1 of the Conditions of the Contract defining the Scope of the Works as being the works described in Part II in the clause numbered 1.

By way of example, as Clause 51(1) stands the Engineer may make any variation which "in his opinion may be necessary". A number of contentious arguments have been conducted as to whether "his opinion" and requirements resulting therefrom are in effect germane to getting the Works completed as was originally intended and defined in the Scope of the Works. It may be more appropriate and equitable to both Parties that a separate contract be entered into to undertake any variation that is of considerable magnitude in relation to the original definition of the Works or specifically outside the Scope of Works.

ENGINEER AND ENGINEER'S REPRESENTATIVE

Duties and powers of the Engineer and Engineer's Representative

clause 2

The duties and responsibility of the Engineer have been described fully in Section 3 but it is of interest to note that these duties are contained in only two lines of print in this particular clause.

However, the important application of this clause is that the Contractor must ensure that the relative clause of Part II of these conditions is completed so that he is aware of those duties for the execution of which the Engineer has, under the terms of his Employment with the Employer, an obligation to obtain prior approval of the Employer.

An example of such a restraint is given below:

"The Engineer must obtain the Employer's approval before the issue of certificates for payment to the Contractor and shall not, without the prior written approval of the Employer, fix new rates, grant any extension of time, or approve any claim for additional payment. The Engineer shall not, without the prior written approval of the Employer, make any modification of the

Works involving extra cost, unless such action is considered necessary in the case of an emergency to ensure the safety of the Works.''

Thus from Part II the Contractor is made fully aware at the time of tender about such restraints and he should be sufficiently prudent to allow in his tender price the unrecoverable cost to him of possible delay waiting for the Employer to approve the Engineer's action.

engineer to 'act fairly'

Because of the very powerful position of the Engineer under the Contract, albeit not a Party to it, a sub-clause should be inserted to oblige the Engineer to act fairly. Such a sub-clause could be modelled on the sub-clause 2.4 in the FIDIC Conditions of Contract for Electrical and Mechanical Works, Second Edition 1980 which reads:

"Wherever by these Conditions the Engineer is required to exercise his discretion, by the giving of a decision, opinion, consent or to express satisfaction or approval, or to determine value or otherwise take action which may affect the rights and obligations of either the Employer or the Contractor the Engineer shall exercise such discretion fairly within the terms of the Contract having regard to all the circumstances. If either party disagrees with the action taken by the Engineer he shall be at liberty to refer the matter to Arbitration in accordance with these Conditions.''

engineer's representative

The Engineer's Representative can undertake many individual and separate functions under the Contract from watching and supervising the Works to such matters as quality control, workmanship and financial control as might be appropriate.   *clause 2(2)*

However, it has been noted that the Engineer's Representative – and there may be more than one in number – is not required to be a person with a particular qualification but simply that he, in the Employer's or Engineer's opinion, is suitable to undertake the tasks he is called upon to perform.

ASSIGNMENT AND SUB-LETTING

assignment

It has been suggested that the assignment of monies to the Contractor's Export Credit Insurers or Guarantors should be permitted also under the terms of this clause.   *clause 3*

sub-letting

This clause as written allows parts of the Works to be sub-let only with the prior approval of the Engineer. However, there are cases when it might be prudent and more convenient to sub-let the whole of the Works, as for example when a foreign contractor has been successful in securing a contract and, after signing the documents, finds it beneficial and politic to sub-let the whole of the Works to a Joint Venture comprised of the successful foreign contractor himself and one or more local contractors.   *clause 4*

Several successful examples of this have occurred in the past and there is no valid reason why this clause should exclude sub-letting the whole of the Works. Suitable new wording can be drafted into Part II of the Contract so as to give the Contractor such an option provided reasonable and appropriate guarantees are given to the Employer to safeguard his position in relation to the Joint Venture.

CONTRACT DOCUMENTS

documents mutually explanatory

It is noted that the provisions of the Conditions of Contract Parts I and II will prevail over those other documents forming part of the Contract and it has been questioned as to which of these two parts takes precedence in the event of a conflict between them.   *clause 5(2)*

It is stated by this sub-clause that the documents themselves which form the Contract are to be taken as mutually explanatory and in the case of ambiguities or discrepancies the same should be explained and adjusted by the Engineer who will issue instructions to the Contractor.

Any costs arising which could not have been reasonably foreseen by the Contractor under the particular circumstances are to be certified by the Engineer and the Employer will pay the Contractor who should also be given an extension of time if appropriate under the circumstances.

However, there is a view that all documents comprising the Contract should not be regarded as mutually explanatory but should be given a status and an order of precedence as follows:

(1) The Agreement
(2) Tender Letter
(3) Letter of Acceptance
(4) Special Conditions of Contract and Appendices (Part II and Part III)
(5) General Conditions of Contract (Part I)
(6) Bills of Quantities
(7) Contract Programme (if any)
(8) Scope of Works
(9) Tender Drawings
(10) Technical Specification
(11) Contract Price Adjustment formula
(12) Schedule of Employer provided materials and drawings.

If this view is adopted it would still mean that the Engineer would issue necessary instructions to the Contractor in the case of ambiguities or discrepancies but it would be more in keeping with the use of the various documents by which the tender price was established for any adjustment to be made in a similar priority to that of the various documents involved.

It would also mean that the Form of Agreement would have to be altered to suit the particular priorities given to the Enterprise concerned.

awings   This clause concerns the ownership and provision of drawings and also   *clause 6* requires the Contractor to give notice to the Engineer when the Works are likely to be delayed or disrupted unless further drawings are issued by the Engineer within a reasonable time.

It has been suggested that Sub-Clause (3) of this clause should state specifically that the Contractor "can rely on receiving the necessary drawings and their approval at such times as are required for the achievement of the approved programme and without the necessity of giving notices." In the case where approval of drawings is necessary it should also state that such approval must be given by the Engineer within a specified time after the submission of such drawings by the Contractor.

In both of these instances it would be reasonable to expect the Contractor to be obligated to give notice as soon as possible if he intends to claim as a result of a failure to perform by the Engineer.

There is noted a discrepancy between Sub-Clauses (3) and (4) in that in the former there is reference to "further drawings or orders, including a direction instruction or approval" whereas in (4) this has been shortened to "any drawing or order" requested by the Contractor. It is suggested that both of these sub-clauses should be consistent and worded the same.

In the event of failing to get any further drawing, order, direction, instruction or approval within a reasonable time and the Contractor suffers delay and incurs costs then the Engineer should take such matters into account in determining any extension of time to which the Contractor is entitled under Clause 44 and the Contractor should be paid the amount of such costs as are reasonable.

Unless there is a requirement to provide as built drawings, operating and maintenance manuals and the like expressed in the Contract or the Specifications then if the Contractor is asked during the course of the Contract to provide these documents this request should be deemed to be a Variant under Clause 51 and payment should be made accordingly.

GENERAL OBLIGATIONS

performance and other bonds

In respect of bonds, of any kind, it is recommended that both Parties should take good advice and study the wording before signing. Each Party should understand the other's point of view. *clause 10*

Conditional bonds are preferable, with specified reasons such as payment on an arbitrator's award, the admission by the Contractor of default or a schedule of reasons why the Contract has been breached. If an on demand bond is required by the Employer, then the Contractor should be allowed to negotiate some of the terms and secure some protection. The Contractor should resist onerous bonding conditions by taking advantage of government or special help such as is provided in the UK by the Export Credits Guarantee Department or Lloyds. The International Chamber of Commerce has issued a set of rules governing the issue and administration of bonds and guarantees.

Full details of the terms of performance bonds, tender bonds, advance payment bonds and any other bonds must be set out in the tender documents so that tenderers can include the cost and implications of these bonds in their tender price. Maintenance bonds and retention bonds requested by the Contractor should be agreed before any Contract is signed.

time for return

Clause 10 does not specify the time when the Performance Bond, or indeed any bond, has to be returned to the Contractor. Because of the different periods of limitation covered by national laws and the need for the Contractor to allow in his tender price for the duration of the validity of the bond a time limit for its release should be specified in Part II of the Conditions of Contract.

If the Contract provides for completion and taking into use part of the Works prior to the time for completion, Clause 10 should provide for the amount of the Performance Bond to be reduced proportionately to the value of the part so completed and taken into use as is the case in Liquidated Damages under Clause 47.

security for performance by employer

Notwithstanding the availability to the Contractor of export credit guarantee insurances there may be circumstances connected with the Employer which might suggest that the Contractor should be provided with a form of Performance Bond by the Employer at his expense on which the former could have recourse in the event of default by the latter – such an arrangement would allow the Contractor to be fully reimbursed in the event of the Employer's liquidation and not for him to be regarded as just another creditor.

inspection of site

Whether or not the Contractor has decided to invest the time and expense of making a visit to the Site the particular wording of this clause is to introduce the word "deemed" which makes the Contractor responsible for the content of his tender whether or not he has undertaken a visit. *clause 11*

If he has visited the Site it is important for the Contractor to recognise that his examination of the Site, its surroundings and any information available in connection with the Site has been made and to his own satisfaction and to an extent which is "so far as is practicable":

Since the word "practicable" can be interpreted in many different ways from being anything which can be done in practice with unlimited resources and available time to just a casual viewing of the Site this Clause should be modified to define that which is "practicable" as being limited to such an inspection and examination which is within acceptable technical limitations and consistent with the economics of so doing.

adverse physical conditions

artificial obstructions

An extract from this particular clause states "which conditions or obstructions could, in his opinion, not have been foreseen by an experienced Contractor...." The problem of this particular wording is the introduction of the words "an experienced Contractor" in that this would seemingly mean any experienced Contractor and not restricting it to the Contractor presenting a tender. It would therefore be only fair that the Employer should recognise that the Contractor he has selected has exercised his best judgement in the forecast of ground on other conditions and that in the event of this clause being implemented then the Employer should not be able to use another Contractor's views as *clause 12* evidence against the appointed Contractor as an argument for rejecting additional payment.

→Also it is recommended that the Engineer should give his decision about the payment of additional costs and the granting of extensions to the time for completion within twenty-eight days from the receipt of the written notice from the Contractor of the existence of the physical conditions or artificial obstructions. ←

Works to be to the satisfaction of the engineer

The Contractor is obliged to execute and maintain the Works in accordance *clause 13* with the Contract and to the "satisfaction" of the Engineer and whilst this is an acceptable arrangement it can be argued that this gives the Engineer too much power.

The clause should be modified to allow that the Contractor's undertaking of the Works should be to the "reasonable" satisfaction of the Engineer and this would avoid the unnecessary holdups to performance and completion when "satisfaction" can often be used to seek a finished standard of completion which is far beyond that which was either necessary or indeed contemplated at the time of tendering but nevertheless could be required by a pedantic Engineer before being satisfied and before certifying acceptance.

Programme

Commentary has already been given in respect of this subject but it must be *clause 14* remembered that the programme referred to by this particular clause is one which "after the acceptance of the tender" is to be submitted for approval to the Engineer showing the order of procedure in which the Contractor intends to carry out the Works.

It is recognised that this approved programme was not part of the tender documents and therefore it cannot be argued that it is upon this programme that the tender was based. If it had been necessary for the Contractor to emphasise by qualification the content of his tender prices as related to the programme upon which he wished the tender to be accepted then it would be up to him at the time of submission to include such a programme and have it accepted as a tender document. Thereafter both the Contractor and the Engineer could be regarded as having a responsibility for ensuring that performance matches the programme.

There is a good case that the programme provided under this particular clause, although intending to show to the Engineer the Contractor's order of procedure in which he proposes to carry out the Works, would be of greater assistance to all concerned if it were to provide more information than just the order of procedure.

It would not be inconsistent for such a programme to be expanded to forecast the required cash flow, to indicate the relationship with any contractors and others engaged on the same Site, to show the timing, the identification and production of those particular key drawings which are required well in advance of executing the actual Work on Site and to define those portions of the Site which the Contractor is to be given at specific times to suit the programme in cases where the entire Site is not available to the Contractor at the time of commencement.

Regrettably the need for drawings and specifications to be given to the Contractor well in advance of work being executed on Site is not always recognised. The lead times for placing firm orders for materials, plant and equipment and for getting them delivered to Site at the right time and in the right condition are in many instances very long and subject to delays. These factors must be recognised early by the Contractor and the Engineer and action taken to ensure delivery on time.

Having been approved by the Engineer then this programme issued under Clause 14 becomes of contractual significance in that any deviations from it in any way whatsoever by either the Contractor or the Engineer could prove supportive or otherwise in matter of performance and possible claims.

Contractor's superintendence Contractor's employees

According to these clauses it is left to the discretion of the Engineer to object *clauses 15 and* to the Contractor's Agent or Representative as well as to any other person *16(2)* employed by the Contractor and for the Engineer to request the removal without any reason being given.

Clearly there should be very good reasons for such a step being taken and also that these should be limited to misconduct, incompetence or negligence. For whatsoever reason the removal of a person is requested the Engineer should be obligated to disclose such reason to the Contractor.

It would also be appropriate for any disagreement on this matter to be referred immediately to the Employer, if the Contractor so wishes, in that without a good acceptable reason being given the person involved might enter into litigation as a result of being removed from the site without the Engineer having notified the Contractor in writing of a fair and valid complaint against the employee.

setting out – need for tolerances

Many arguments have arisen on sites – especially when distances and areas are large – between the Contractor and the Engineer over the location of a point in space. The Contractor's surveyor has identified the point using his instruments and starting from the original points, lines and levels given by the Engineer; the latter's surveyors check this point from the same base data and disagree with the Contractor's setting out. The respective site staff involved spend much time and effort trying to reconcile the difference. In most cases it is forgotten in the heat of the argument that all survey measurement work can be done only within certain tolerances, which must be recognised and specified in relation to the order of the distances and climatic circumstances. Thus the difference between the Contractor's original setting out and the check by the Engineer in most cases will be found to be within the tolerances defined for the particular situation. A decision has to be made on the spot to agree the location of the point in question and not waste time blaming each other.

clause 17

Engineers and manufacturers must also bear in mind the existence of tolerances in setting out and the need to avoid specifying and designing details of plant, equipment and structures to such a fine degree of tolerance as to be impossible to achieve in practice.

general comments on indemnities, obligations and insurances

Whether included in the contract or not – the Employer, contractors, subcontractors, suppliers and the professional consultant team all have their responsibilities at law, under the contract or otherwise for such matters as:

clauses 20, 21, 22, 23 and 24

(a) loss or damage to the contract Works or the failure to meet requirements of the Contract and any financial consequences thereof.

(b) liability at law for death or injury to third parties or loss of or damage to their property, either during the construction/erection/installation programme or thereafter.

(c) liability at law for death of or injury to their employees in the course of their employment.

Unfortunately accidents, failures and unforeseen events will happen during construction contracts and in any accident involving injury or damage on or to a construction site there are many potential defendants: the Employer, the Contractor, the sub-contractor, the consultants, plant hire contractors – any of whom could be held responsible. Suppose the law were left to take its normal course then the various parties would all be potential defendants, with each trying to prove it was not his fault.

An indemnity clause requires one party to indemnify the other party to the contract against defined injuries, losses or claims. These clauses do not change legal responsibility – they simply change financial responsibility. For example, one can be negligent and, in law, liable to pay, but because of the indemnity clause the other party pays the bill.

An obligation or responsibility clause states who, in certain circumstances, accepts responsibility for loss or damage to the contract works.

An insurance clause lays down who, in given circumstances, will insure and for whose benefit and against specified perils. Such a clause does not change or move legal responsibility, it simply provides the pool of money out of which the person responsible is able to draw funds to satisfy the claim.

In general it is the Contractor who is required to arrange the insurances but there is a tendency nowadays for the Employer to procure a form of "umbrella" policy to cover himself, contractors, sub-contractors, suppliers, plant hirers and project managers and consultant advisers. FIDIC Project Insurance Committee issued a Status Report in December 1981 on the insurance of large engineering projects which is relevant to this subject.

Whichever way it is done the other party to the contract must check that the responsible party has arranged the insurances adequately to suit everybody involved in the Works and, of course, avoid duplication of cover.

olicies involved The principal contractor's all risks policy covers against loss or damage to the contract Works but other policies may be obtained covering other risks as follows.

(1) "Constructional Plant" policy covering: loss or damage to constructional plant (i.e. plant, such as excavators, used in the course of constructing the Works)

(2) "Plant Erection" or "Erection All Risks" policy covering: loss of or damage to such as a tower crane which itself has to be erected or assembled on the site of the Works

(3) "Goods in Transit" policy covering: loss of or damage to plant, equipment and materials during transit and incidental storage off-site

(4) "Employer's Liability" policy covering: the insured's liability to pay compensation for bodily injury to his employees arising in the course of their employment (usually in countries in which there are no workmen's compensation acts)

(5) "Public Liability" policy covering: the insured's liability to pay compensation for bodily injury to third parties or loss of or damage to their property.

The cover provided under a construction policy does not usually include that obtainable under other policies such as :

(a) "Marine" policy covering: loss of or damage to ships or cargo; liabilities arising from the use of vessels

(b) "Aviation" policy covering: loss of or damage to air cargo or aircraft; liabilities arising from the use of aircraft

(c) "Motor" policy covering: loss of or damage to vehicles constructed to transport persons or property by road or rail; liability for injury, loss or damage arising from the ownership, possession or use of such vehicles

(d) "Workmen's Compensation" policy covering: an insured's liability to pay compensation for bodily injury to his employees arising in the course of their employment

(e) "Professional Indemnity" policy covering: liabilities of architects, consulting engineers, and other professional persons for the consequences of their errors and omissions

(f) "Consequential Loss" policy covering: consequential losses (other than the cost of reinstatement) arising from loss of or damage to the Works or constructional plant

(g) "Contract Performance Guarantee" bond protecting: the Employer against failure of the Contractor to fulfil his obligations under the contract

(h) Tender bonds, advance payment bonds, retention bonds and maintenance guarantees: all or some of these are provided by contractors to protect the Employer as in (g) above.

n insured A sum insured under the contract works policy is usually a fixed sum which is the limit up to which insurers will pay. Thus the sum insured must be the maximum possible loss to which the Contractor may be exposed. If the worst happens and there is a total loss the Contractor must have sufficient money to rebuild the Works. As the loss may occur at the end of the contract period – which may be several years – the reinstatement value covered by the insurance must allow for future inflation.

It is no use insuring a sum equal to the Contract Price if total loss can be foreseen occurring at the end of the contract period with reinstatement taking another few years to accomplish. On the other hand, especially where parts of the Works are taken over or into use by the Employer during the contract period, or the Works are such as they cannot be totally destroyed – then a maximum loss has to be estimated and insurance cover purchased to cover this loss.

Similarly with public liability policies the Contract may state that insurance has to be arranged up to a given limit of indemnity. The specification of such a limit does not release the Contractor from his obligations as the indemnity clause itself does not limit the Contractor's exposure. It is therefore very important for the Contractor to make sure that the public liability insurance limit is adequate. If deemed to be inadequate then the Contractor should insure to cover a greater sum in order to protect himself.

It is also wise to keep public liability policies operational and not necessarily let them lapse as soon as the Contract has been completed. Damage is insured under these policies only when it occurs during the period of insurance. Another important point to bear in mind is that damage has to be accidental in order to recover costs under the public liability insurance – damage which is not accidental but inevitable is not covered e.g. damage to surrounding properties caused by piling or deep excavation.

general

In any major project the risks and insurance policies which can arise, such as the Contractor's Employer's liability policy, the public liability policy, the Contract Works policy and the professional negligence policies result in many complications. Piecing together particular policies to ensure there is no gap through which risks can fall can be very difficult. Hence the necessity, if one is the Employer, to examine the Contractor's policies; or, if the Contractor, working to an Employer arranged policy, to study any policy taken out by the Employer and for both to ensure that all risks are adequately covered.

care of works excepted risks insurance of works, etc.

Clauses 20 and 21 do not make a clear distinction between the responsibility for the care of the Works and the necessity to insure against certain risks. *clauses 20 and 21*

These clauses should be redrafted to clarify the following principles more precisely.

(1) The Contractor is responsible for the Works up to the date stated in the Certificte of Completion and is responsible for the repair of all damage prior to that date except for damage caused by any of the excepted risks to be defined in Clause 20, Sub-Clause (2).

(2) The excepted risks for which the Contractor is not responsible for repairing damage caused thereby should be:
(a) risks outside the control of both Parties such as war, hostilities, etc.
(b) forces of nature which an experienced contractor could not reasonably foresee
(c) use or occupation by the Employer
(d) the Engineer's design of the Works.

(3) Where an excepted risk together with causes for which the Contractor is responsible have caused any loss or damage, an apportionment of the cost of rectification should be made based on an assessment of the extent to which these causes have contributed to the loss or damage. This would mean also that apportionment of damages should be made if the Engineer's design has been a part cause of the loss or damage.

(4) Which Party insures the Works has no bearing on the responsibility for the care of the Works; responsibility for the care of and responsibility for the insurance of the Works have to be clearly defined. The insurance cover requested by the Employer should be specified in Part II – Conditions of Particular Application.

damage to persons and property

Similarly the basic concept of Clauses 22 and 23 in respect of damages to Persons and Property should be revised and clarified. *clauses 22 and 23*

hird party
nsurance

In the event of concurrent liability an apportionment of damages should be made.

Independently of the question of liabilities the insurance cover to be taken out by the Contractor should be specified in Part II Conditions of Particular Application.

ossils etc

As written this clause only allows the Contractor to carry out, at the expense of the Employer, the Engineer's Representative's orders as to the disposal of the fossils etc. It does not count the cost to the Contractor of implementing the other requirements of the clause and the costs of being instructed to undertake work resulting from the intervention of outside or government authorities who are interested in the fossils, coins, articles of value or antiquity etc.   *clause 27*

It is considered appropriate that all work arising from the implementation of this clause should be considered as a Variation and covered by Clauses 40, 44, 51 and 52 as appropriate i.e. suspension, extension of time for completion and variations respectively.

atent rights
nd royalties

As at present worded, this clause states that the Contractor is fully responsible for the infringement of patent or similar rights even if the infringement is due to the design of the Engineer or concerned with materials supplied or specified by the Employer or the Engineer.   *clause 28*

This is an unfair liability to be placed upon the Contractor and it should be corrected by requiring that the Employer on his part warrants that any design or instructions given by him or the Engineer shall not in any way cause the Contractor to infringe any patents, registered designs, copyrights, trade marks, or industrial property rights in the performance of the Contract. In the event of an infringement arising due to the design or instructions given by the Employer or the Engineer then the liability should rest with the Employer and he should indemnify the Contractor.

pportunities
r other
ntractors

This clause places upon the Contractor an obligation to afford all reasonable opportunities for other contractors employed by the Employer to carry out their works not only on Site but "near the Site" – this also applies to the workmen of the Employer and any other duly constituted Authorities.   *clause 31*

Other than what might be regarded as "reasonable opportunities" being afforded it is a requirement for the Engineer or his Representative to give the Contractor a written request for permission to use such items as Contractor's scaffolding or other plant on Site or to provide any other service of whatever nature together with access for which the Employer – and not the other contractors involved – will pay to the Contractor such sums as, in the opinion of the Engineer, may be reasonable.

In the event of this clause being implemented it would be prudent for the Contractor to look immediately into his position as relating to the various insurances he is carrying in connection with the Contract and also with his employees and to make certain that if other contractors are employed on Site that he should be indemnified by the Employer for any claims. He should also ensure that should he be delayed because of the presence of such other contractors then he would seek an extension of time as a special circumstance under Clause 44.

If possible it would be advantageous to both Parties if the activities of others on or near the site were to be described in detail in the tender documents and certainly as soon as possible after the commencement of the Works.

ntractor to
eep site clear

'earance of site
n completion

These two clauses embody much sound commonsense and good housekeeping. There is no quarrel with the wording of the clauses nor with the intentions. Nevertheless it was felt prudent to add some comments on the implementation of these clauses by the Contractor. The road to Hell is paved with good intentions and all Contractors recognise the need for and intend to keep the site clear and remove everything at the end of the job. However it is wise to honour these two clauses literally.   *clauses 32 and*
33

Keeping the site clear, recovering re-usable materials and equipment, maintaining access roads, fences, lighting and communications must be good practice. Unfortunately construction sites are notorious for the poor quality of their working conditions. Clearance of the site on completion must never be left until completion because by then it is too late. This applies especially when plant, equipment and materials are the property of the Employer.

It is not unreasonable to start planning and undertaking clearance of the site about half way through the period of construction. The logistics of recovering plant, equipment and materials require careful study so that the salvage and clearance operations do not interfere with the programme of execution of the Works – nevertheless recovery and clearance work must be allowed for in the tender price.

MATERIALS AND WORKMANSHIP

inspection of operations

clause 37

This clause deals primarily with the arrangement of access whereby the Engineer or any person authorised by him shall be given access to the Works and places where work is being prepared or for such places where materials, manufactured articles or machinery are being obtained for the Works.

Whilst this is a reasonable obligation to be placed upon the Contractor nevertheless it should be qualified that "at all times" should be changed to "at all reasonable times".

It is also to be noted that whereas the Contractor is to provide access as such to the Works this differs in him not being called upon to afford access to such places of manufacture but where he "shall afford every facility for, and every assistance in, or in obtaining the right of such access" – again this should be limited to "all reasonable times".

In respect of the conduct of the Engineer and any authorised person in the inspection of operations it should be required that the persons should be obliged to respect the confidentiality of any manufacturing secrets or know-how which they learn as a result of their visit.

removal of improper work and materials – default of contractor in compliance

clause 39

At any time during the progress of the Works this clause empowers the Engineer to order in writing that the Contractor must remove materials which are not suitable, replace them with proper materials and remove and re-erect any work which the Engineer states is not in accordance with the Contract.

Furthermore sub-clause 39(2) entitles the Employer, should the Contractor be in default in carrying out the Engineer's order, to employ and pay other persons to carry out the Engineer's order and to recover such costs from the Contractor.

The Contractor is obliged under Clause 8 to execute the Works with due care and diligence and to the Engineer's satisfaction as required by Clause 13 so it seems strange that the Employer is given the right to employ other persons if the Contractor is in default in carrying out the order of the Engineer in accordance with Clause 39. The Contractor's right to challenge the Engineer's order seems to be disregarded albeit that the Contractor is obliged to construct the Works properly under Clauses 8 and 13 and must do so anyway in order to secure a Certificate of Completion under Clause 48.

Clause 39 needs further clarification so that the Contractor can register his disagreement with the Engineer's order and recover his costs if the Engineer is proved wrong. It is better that the default in carrying out the order can be defined precisely and that the Engineer must give a time within which the Contractor is required to carry out the order. Only Sub-Clause 39(1) (a) refers to time or times as may be specified in the order for the removal of materials.

As written, Clause 39 gives the power to the Engineer to issue an order in writing to the Contractor – can this be considered as giving rise to a dispute under Clause 67 if the Contractor disagrees with the Engineer's order? And should the Engineer be the judge of his own actions as provided by Clause 67?

suspension of the works

clause 40

It can happen, and it often does, when the Engineer orders the suspension of the Works under Clause 40 that, beyond the order to stop work, the Engineer issues no further instructions during the suspension period. In these circumstances it is not possible for the Contractor to claim the extra cost incurred in giving effect to the Engineer's instructions. It would seem reasonable, therefore, that the Contract should be worded to ensure that the Engineer issues such further instructions as are necessary to cover the measures required to be taken by the Contractor during the suspension period.

Sub-Clause 40(1) (c) prevents the Contractor from claiming suspension costs if the suspension is due to climatic conditions on site. This is in conflict with Clauses 20 and 40(1) (d) because if the climatic conditions are considered as forces of nature then the Contractor might be freed from a responsibility for care of the Works as it is an excepted risk (Clause 20) and similarly under Sub-Clause 40(1) (d) he can claim suspension costs.

Thus the climatic conditions in Sub-Clause 40(1) (c) need to be qualified to be foreseeable if the Contractor is not to be allowed to claim suspension costs. If the climatic conditions are not foreseeable by an experienced contractor or out of character with the seasonal averages then the Contractor should be able to re-cover his costs of complying with the Engineer's instructions under this Clause 40.

COMMENCEMENT TIME AND DELAYS

mmencement
works

Contractors have complained that having signed the Agreement there can be a period of time, which seemingly is without a defined limit, within which an order from the Engineer to commence the Works on Site, within the period named in the Appendix to the Tender, should be given.

clause 41

It can be that an inordinate delay by the Engineer in issuing an order to commence might completely alter the Contractor's concept of pricing particularly when a late start can involve an additional winter's working which he otherwise had no reason to anticipate.

Having once commenced he is then obliged to proceed with due expedition and without delay except as may be expressly sanctioned or ordered by the Engineer or be wholly beyond the Contractor's control.

It has been suggested that there are two modifications necessary to this Clause. The first being that there should be a time specified within which the Engineer must give an order to commence and if failing so to do, then the Contractor should have the right to have the Contract deemed to have been frustrated or to take an option to re-negotiate the Contract Price.

The second is that the Engineer when issuing an order for commencement should state that all of any conditions precedent to the final signing of the Agreement have been fulfilled to the satisfaction of both Parties. Until this can be stated then the Engineer should not issue an order to commence the Works on Site.

ctensions of
me for
mpletion

Extensions of the time for the completion of the Works are the subject of this clause and the procedure for dealing with the Contractor's claim is set out also. However, no reference is made to the Contractor's right to claim for the extra costs associated with any extension determined by the Engineer. Presumably the Contractor can submit claims for extra costs so incurred as allowed for in Sub-Clause 52(5) and prior to the issue of the Maintenance Certificate as set out in Sub-Clause 62(2). Possibly the law applicable to the Contract may provide for extra costs to be claimed due to extensions in time.

clause 44

It is suggested that, to clarify this point which generates misunderstandings and uncertainties in practice, the words "notwithstanding the right to claim for extra costs associated with extension in time" should be incorporated in an appropriate place in the clause.

Occasionally special circumstances due to the default of the Contractor are associated with other special circumstances which are not due to any failure on the part of the Contractor. On such occasions it is recommended that an extension of time for completion of the Works should be determined by the Engineer which is related to the contribution to the delay attributable to the other special circumstances.

quidated
amages for
elay

In the event of the Contractor failing to achieve completion within the period stated in the Appendix or within any extended time as may be allowed under Clause 44, the Contractor has to pay the Employer the sum stated in the

clause 47

Contract as liquidated damages – whether or not this is paid as such or whether it is deducted by the Employer from monies due to the Contractor is optional.

The Engineer is not required to issue any form of certification stating that the Contractor has failed to achieve completion on time nor is it part of his responsibility to make a reduction in any payment certificates or indeed in the final account by the amount of the sums calculated as being liquidated damages – it is solely the prerogative of the Employer to settle the matter with the Contractor when he has failed to achieve completion on time.

It therefore seems a matter of considerable importance that in the event of the Contractor being entitled to an extension of time for completion under Clause 44 that he should be notified by the Engineer of the amount of any extensions within a period of say twenty-eight days. To delay the granting of an extension of time could put the Employer in a position of deducting liquidated damages only to find that subsequently an extension of time has been issued by the Engineer which requires a repayment to be made to the Contractor.

It has been suggested that the recovery of liquidated damages by the Employer might be made only after the Engineer has announced the final number of days of extension he has determined under Clause 44 to be added to the time for completion and so establish the actual number of days delay. This would encourage the Engineer to determine the amount of extension of time more speedily.

However, it must not be forgotten that the Contractor is obliged to complete the Works properly and on time under Clauses 8, 13, 41 and 43.

liquidated damages – genuine assessment

Liquidated damages are intended to be a genuine pre-estimate of loss if the Works are not completed on time. Some large public authorities often quantify the liquidated damages on the basis of loss of assets and an assessment of the interest on capital expended, even if they do not have any actual costs if the contract is not finished on time. This is not a genuine pre-estimate of loss. Indeed in some cases the failure to complete on time may result in saving in cost to an Employer, e.g. a water pumping scheme using a large amount of electricity and involving increased maintenance and operating costs.   *clause 47*

Such authorities risk the danger of having their claim for liquidated damages rejected. If it is so important that the scheme is completed on time for other than financial reasons then it would be better to use a penalty/bonus clause to encourage the Contractor to finish the Works within the time for completion. Part II makes provision for the inclusion of such a bonus clause.

When deciding the amount of liquidated damages to be inserted into Appendix II before tenders are invited the Employer must study the commercial implications of the decision bearing in mind the demands for work by contractors in the construction market. Should the liquidated damages be set high or realistic and tend to increase tender prices or should they be pitched at a lower and modest level which could represent in fact a reduction of the Contractor's liabilities if causing a delay?

The Employer should bear in mind also that Sub-Clause 47(2) provides for the liquidated damages to be reduced as parts of the Works are certified by the Engineer as completed and occupied or used by the Employer. Towards the end of the time for completion if large parts of the Works have been taken into use the amount of liquidated damages remaining could be very small indeed and would not give the Employer much power to force the Contractor to complete the Works in their entirety on time.

Some legal advisers recommend that the liquidated damages clause be removed completely so that Employers would recover damages for delay through the courts with proof of delay having to be established in the normal way. However, the Employer would have to wait for a settlement and not have the ability to recover some damages on completion as he can under Clause 47.

Whereas in most contracts the variation of price clauses enable the Contractor to keep up with inflation the Employer has no opportunity to adjust the amount of liquidated damages in the same way. Presumably the Employer added some allowance for inflation when he assessed the amount for insertion into the Appendix before inviting tenders.

The subject matter of Clause 48 is referred to as a Certification of Completion in respect of the Works which on detailed reading is found not to be so – it really covers a situation when the whole of the Works or, where otherwise appropriate, a section or substantial part of the Permanent Works has been "substantially" completed and has passed any final tests which may be specified within the Contract.

The comment is directed to the conflict between "completed" Works and to a situation where such Works have been only "substantially" completed although linked with an undertaking given by the Contractor to complete the unfinished Works during the Period of Maintenance.

It has been suggested that the Certificate of Completion should be more correctly worded as "Certificate of Substantial Completion" so as to avoid any misunderstanding.

Sub-Clause 48(2) (b) concerns itself with any part of the Permanent Works which has been substantially completed and occupied or used by the Employer. In case of occupation or use by the Employer it is not relevant that the Permanent Works have been completed or not – such occupation or use should only be with the prior written consent of the Contractor unless the Engineer has issued a Certificate of Completion for the relevant part. If the Employer occupies or uses a part of the Works with or without the prior consent of the Contractor then that part of the Works should be deemed to have been completed and the Engineer must issue the Certificate of Completion as from the date of such occupation or use. The Engineer can specify all the outstanding Works which have to be done during the Period of Maintenance.

Any additional costs incurred by the Contractor as a result of the prior occupation or use of the Works by the Employer should be borne by the Employer.

A suitable modification to this sub-clause should be made to cover this situation.

It is necessary to make proper provision for the obligation under Clause 48(4) which deems that, notwithstanding a Certificate of Completion being given, there still remains a query in respect of any "section or part of the Permanent Works" remaining outstanding before the completion of the whole of the Works in that the Certificate of Completion is not deemed to certify completion of any ground or surface requiring reinstatement unless the Certificate states so expressly – it is not defined what happens when such ground or surfaces requiring reinstatement have been reinstated finally.

It has been suggested that there is a need to introduce another sub-clause which would cover the release of the first half of the Retention Money in that there is no reference to such release found anywhere in the Conditions although provision could be said to have been contemplated within Part II.

The introduction of such a new sub-clause would make it clear that the Engineer, when issuing a Certificate of Completion albeit only of a substantial nature, would initiate the release of the first half of the Retention Money. Any liability of the Contractor to correct defects etc. or undertake additional work can be considered covered adequately by the second part of the Retention Money.

MAINTENANCE AND DEFECTS

It is intended that as soon as practicable after the expiration of the Period of Maintenance that the Contractor shall "deliver to the Employer" the Works as originally required under the Contract with the exception of fair wear and tear.

This is inappropriate wording in that when the Engineer issued a Certificate of Completion under Clause 48 it was for the Works to have been "delivered" in effect to the Employer. At the same time the Employer took over the responsibility for the care of the Works which have been satisfactorily completed and occupied.

However, once the Period of Maintenance has expired the Engineer is to be satisfied that the Works are once again in the same condition as when delivered

Certificate of completion of Works

clause 48

Consent of contractor to occupation by Employer

clause 48(2) (b)

Ground or surface reinstatement

clause 48(4)

New sub-clause about release of retention monies

clause 48

Period of maintenance and work of repair

clause 49(1) (2) and (3)

and that the Contractor, during the Period of Maintenance or immediately there-after, has executed all work of repair, amendment, reconstruction etc., together with other scheduled outstanding work still to be done at the time of substantial completion which has been ordered by the Engineer and which was necessitated by causes outside the responsibility and control of the Contractor.

It has been noted that payment for such work is to be regarded as if it were additional work from which it must be assumed as being a Variation under Clause 51(1). This cannot be so because when the Engineer issued the Certificate of Completion under Clause 48 then the opportunity for him to order further Variations under Clause 51(1) was denied.

If it was intended that the payment for this work was to be made on the same basis as "additional work" under Clause 51 it should have been so stated. Such an intention would be unfair and the Contractor must argue that his rates as quoted are not for such further work and that they can relate only to doing work before the Period of Maintenance commenced and not during or after and it follows therefore that there are no rates in the Bills of Quantities which can be considered appropriate. He should therefore expect to be paid the actual costs he incurred plus overheads and profit irrespective as to whether the value bears any relationship to the original unit rates or not.

clause 49(1) The expression "Period of Maintenance" is referred to in the Appendix to the Conditions and whilst the sub-clauses deal with the matter as to the Contractor's obligations during this time and also the subject of payment it has been suggested that the "Period of Maintenance" should be re-titled throughout the Conditions as being the "Period of defect liability and guarantee" in that this is more appropriate and removes the sometimes held opinion that all "maintenance" is to the Contractor's expense.

This would not alter the definition and application of the "Maintenance Certificate" referred to in Clauses 61 and 62.

Employers should be reminded that because the Contractor is obliged to carry out corrective or additional work during the Maintenance Period their position can be expensive if the Works which have been occupied are put out of operation during that period as a result of the Contractor's operations.

The Contractor is not called upon to meet any of the Employer's costs or damages suffered during the period of carrying out the obligations of Clause 49 because any such work carried out by the Contractor at his own expense must be confined to the "work" as such and not to consequential effects.

ALTERATIONS, ADDITIONS AND OMISSIONS

variations This clause gives the Engineer the authority to make any variation which in his *clause 51* opinion is necessary and states that the value, if any, of these variations will be taken into account as an adjustment to the Contract Price.

It should, however, be noted that other variations affecting the Contract Price can take place which are not necessarily covered by the use of this particular Clause. For example when implementing Clause 12 any additional work arising is not to be dealt with as a Variation and the costs incurred should be certified by the Engineer and paid by the Employer.

This being a realistic approach as in the case of Clause 12 the additional costs arising should be assessed in relation to the special unforeseen circumstances giving rise to the additional work and not be related necessarily to rates in the Bills of Quantities.

Insofar as the present working of Clause 51(1) is concerned there are complaints that it requires correction and the reasoning behind this dissatisfaction is that because of the wide discretionary power accorded to the Engineer entitling him to make any variation of the form, quality, or quantity of the work it should be limited to at least two respects. The powers granted to the Engineer by Sub-Clause 51(1) therefore need to be qualified in some degree and it is suggested that the following two provisions might be written into the Clause:

(a) A proviso should be included to the effect that the Engineer is not entitled to change the general character, quality or kind of work unless the Contractor expressly agrees

(b) The Engineer should not be empowered to order the execution of the work for which the Contractor does not have the necessary capability, qualification, nor financial resources so to do.

ders in *riting*

clause 51(2)

There is obviously a confusion in Clause 51(2) in that it sets out specifically that "no such Variations will be made by the Contractor without an order in writing from the Engineer". It then proceeds to contradict this by saying "provided that no order in writing shall be required to increase or decrease the quantity of any work where such an increase or decrease is not the result of an order given under this Clause". It is further confusing in that notwithstanding the original obligation that the Contractor has to be given a written order it then states that "should the Engineer consider it desirable to give any such order verbally the Contractor shall comply with such order and any confirmation of such verbal orders as given by the Engineer". It is yet even more confusing because if the confirmation made within seven days by the Contractor to the Engineer of the order he has received is not contradicted in 14 days it shall be deemed to be an order in writing from the Engineer.

This leaves the unanswered question as to what happens when the Contractor has not confirmed a verbal order within seven days – does the order stand or is it considered to be never given as such? – is the Contractor denied payment only on an interim basis but is paid as and when the Final Account is settled? This reasoning has support in that the Final Account should represent the total value of the work performed.

table rates *d prices*

clause 52(1) and (2)

It has not escaped comment that this Sub-Clauses 52(1) and (2) leave unanswered the question as to what is a "suitable rate or price" really means. Arguments have developed as to whether this is to be construed as being in relation to those rates already existing in the Bills of Quantities and does "suitable" mean "analogous"? It should not be forgotten that the reason for seeking a new rate is only because the existing rates are "unreasonable or inapplicable" so these as such cannot be related to such existing rates.

New rates should be calculated therefore as at the original base date of the tender in order that any Price Adjustment formulae can be applied properly.

ne limit for *aluating* *riations*

Insofar as Clause 52 is concerned no time limit is specified within which the evaluation of the work arising from variations is to be made. This should be corrected and the Engineer required to provide an evaluation of the Variation in the same monthly period as Certificates for Payment are required to be produced.

It would also be appropriate at the same time to examine such Variations with particular reference to Clause 52(2) and to see if any other rate or price contained in the Bills of Quantities is rendered unreasonable or inapplicable because of the issue of a particular Variation.

Clause 52 is also unsatisfactory to Specialist companies engaged in such works as chemical or alluvium grouting by injection because the quantities shown in the Bills of Quantities can be considered only at the best as a reasonable guess and at the worst as being very inaccurate. This situation arises because the assumptions made about the characteristics of various geological formations together with other problems combine to make even an approximate estimate of quantities of doubtful value.

However, an estimate of quantities of some sort must be given to complete the Bills of Quantities in order to obtain a tender.

In the event it has been found many times that the quantities and rates of progress estimated are totally inappropriate for the work ultimately required. Arguments then follow as to whether the price or unit rate for the work is in itself unrealistic and whether, whenever a Variation is ordered, such a price or unit rate is to be used to evaluate the work involved.

Under these circumstances a more equitable version of variation evaluation should apply when dealing with specialist work.

MEASUREMENT

lump sums

In general the Third Edition of these FIDIC Conditions deals only with Works *clauses 55, 56* which are the subject of admeasurement to determine the final contract price and the quantities stated in the Bills are approximate. However there can be lump sum contracts and mixed contracts which contain lump sums and bills of quantities. In such contracts provision must be made to allow the valuation of variations to be assessed and agreed. Possibly a separate schedule of rates might be provided by the Contractor solely for the purpose of evaluating variations to a lump sum contract with a proviso, of course, that special circumstances might increase or decrease the quoted rates.

time for measurement

Clause 56, in particular, determines that measurement is the prerogative of *clause 56* the Engineer and that he decides when the measurements are to be made.

The Contractor is entitled to be present when the measurements are made. It would seem more reasonable and to the benefit of the Employer and to the Contractor that the time of measurement should be agreed so that the Engineer can measure jointly with the Contractor. There may be merit also in having a provision to require either the Engineer or the Contractor to request the joint measurement of any part of the Works at any time – especially when the part involved is likely to be covered up or removed.

change in quantities

Some other standard conditions for construction works contain a sub-clause *other standard* which provides for the circumstances when the actual quantities measured *conditions* during the course of the Works for any particular item are greater or less than those stated in the Bill of Quantities and of such magnitude that, if in the opinion of the Engineer, there is a case for re-negotiation of the rates, then he determines (after consultation with the Contractor) an appropriate increase or decrease in any rates rendered unreasonable or inapplicable as a result of the change in quantities.

There may be merit and advantages to both Parties if the above referred-to sub-clause used in other standard conditions were to be included in these Conditions to cover changes in quantities stated in the Bill of Quantities.

Such a new sub-clause need not affect Sub-Clause 52(3) of these FIDIC *clause 52(3)* Conditions which covers changes in the Contract Price exceeding 10% up or down of the sum named in the Letter of Acceptance – or such other percentage as may be agreed at the time of tender.

NOMINATED SUB-CONTRACTORS

nominated sub-contractors

The employment of nominated Sub-Contractors can be a source of disputes and, *clause 59* in general, it is thought, should be avoided.

If the Employer or Engineer insists upon nomination then pre-contract nomination or selection is a much simpler proposition since the tenderers are aware of the facts at the time of preparing their bids rather than having to allow for the unknown nomination and having only a provisional sum to guide them. Pre-contract nomination will then place on the potential Contractor the burden of securing a suitable Sub-Contract offer from the Nominated Sub-Contractor before he makes his own tender offer. Nevertheless the Engineer or the Employer will need to ensure in advance that the nominated Sub-Contractor can perform his obligations to suit the eventual Contractor's programme.

If the Employer retains the right for nomination it should be clearly stated what happens in the event of the Nominated Sub-Contractor entering liquidation or being unable to continue with the fulfilment of his obligations.

In the event of the above situation arising it has been suggested that:

(a) the Employer should be obliged to re-nominate
(b) that he should pay the Contractor any additional costs incurred
(c) that an appropriate extension of time should be given.

It is known that within the United Kingdom this matter has been settled in law but in those countries where this is not so then the above requirements set out in precise detail will avoid unnecessary litigation.

CERTIFICATES AND PAYMENT

This clause, although contained within Part I, provides no information whatsoever on the subject of certificates and payments but directs attention to Part II and the Clause numbered 60 which has to cover the wide range of subjects which are involved in both certificates and payments and which need to be itemised and particularly detailed in order that Clause 60 in Part II can be implemented successfully. *clause 60*

It is recognised in practice that no payment will be made by the Employer unless the Engineer issues the appropriate Certificate and whilst the Appendix deals with the need for the Employer to honour such certificates within a specific time there is no mention of the time within which the Engineer should be required to issue such certificates after receipt of an application for payment from the Contractor. It is suggested that unless specifically stated otherwise all certificates of the Engineer for payment should be issued by him within a time limit of twenty eight days following receipt of the Contractor's application for payment.

Furthermore it should be emphasised that there should be no withholding of certificates or payments on account in respect of work which has been performed but contains some work which is considered unacceptable to the Engineer. Full payment should be made in respect of the acceptable work with no or part payment for the work which was not to the entire satisfaction of the Engineer.

Whereas the approval of the Works being constituted only by the Maintenance Certificate may satisfy the principles of English Law other laws, especially European ones, consider that approval of the Works is given by the taking over of the Works by the Employer or by the issue of the Certificate of Completion of the Works under Clause 48. Thus under other laws the Maintenance Certificate only advises the Employer that the Engineer is satisfied that the obligations of the Contractor to remedy defects etc. during the Period of Maintenance have been fulfilled. A possible revision of Clauses 48 and 61 might be made therefore to clarify this point and so be more compatible with contract laws other than those based on English Law. Clause 62 may need to be modified if the above two clauses are rewritten. *clause 61*

FRUSTRATION

"Frustration", it is thought, being peculiar to the English legal system should not be used in International Standard Conditions. The use of the expression 'force majeure' would be better in the circumstances. *clause 66*

SETTLEMENT OF DISPUTES

It should be made clear under this clause or under Part II Clause numbered 60 that, when the Engineer certifies payment in accordance with Clause 60, the Employer may not dispute the certificate and submit the dispute to arbitration in accordance with Clause 67. The Contractor must be allowed to rely upon the Engineer's Certificates for payment and regard them as binding upon the Employer. *clause 67*

Whilst the existing Clause 67 provides a method by which disputes may be settled through arbitration the wording is somewhat tortuous. It would be easier to follow if the procedure were set out as a tabulated procedure rather than as written. *new clause*

However, there may be another way of resolving disputes which is simpler and less costly than arbitration. It is suggested that an independent expert might be appointed for each contract or whenever a dispute arises who would give an immediate decision on any dispute which, if either Party disagreed, could be challenged by the implementation of Clause 67. Such an independent expert might be an engineer, a member of a professional practice or anyone having appropriate qualifications and experience. The expenses of such an appointment might be shared between the Parties.

Whilst it may not be possible to force an outsider to investigate and rule on any dispute the Parties should be able to agree the appointment of an independent expert to examine the dispute and give a verdict. It is hoped that the Parties would agree to accept the verdict as final and binding but if this is not possible then the Parties are better informed and better able to judge whether or not to go to arbitration. If they do agree upon this final measure then they do so knowing that the issue will have been examined and clarified.

One very important aspect of the timely use of an independent expert is that he would be able to study the facts and events giving rise to the dispute very soon after they had arisen and in many cases before the work under investigation had been covered up or removed. He would be able also to speak to the people involved when their memories were fresh and not, as in the case with arbitration, maybe several years after the contract had been completed. Likewise these people would be on Site and not scattered over the four corners of the world.

The independent expert would not be required to behave as an arbitrator – his role would be much more in the capacity of a conciliator. His duty is to establish the facts, examine the documents concerned, meet each Party separately as well as jointly and be able to give full time to the task so as to arrive at a decision as speedily as possible.

His objective would be to persuade both Parties that his decisions are correct so they are reluctant to proceed to arbitration. The independent expert needs to give detailed reasons setting out how he has arrived at his conclusion and why he feels his verdict is sound and should be acceptable to both Parties.

Such conciliation is worth trying as it is much quicker and cheaper than the alternative arbitration or litigation.

EMPLOYER'S REPRESENTATIVE

The Engineer and the Contractor are permitted – almost obliged – to appoint *new clause* representatives whose duties are defined in the Conditions of Contract. The Employer, who is responsible for initiating, financing and ultimately controlling the use of the Enterprise, is not required to do this but it has been suggested that he should also be required to nominate a Representative whose name can be introduced into the Conditions – Part II in the Clause numbered 1.

The relationships between the Engineer, the Employer's Representative and the Contractor should be defined very clearly to ensure that there is no possible conflict with the responsibilities already existing in the Contract.

It is not intended that the Employer's Representative would overrule any of the powers and authorities given to the Engineer but he would play an authoritative role in circumstances where the Enterprise might benefit by a collective exchange of views in order that decisions may be made which might benefit the short or long term use of the Enterprise.

From the point of view of the Engineer or the Contractor it is much better to have to deal with one person acting for the Employer than with an amorphous committee or body whose interests can be legion depending upon which member is in the ascendancy at any one time.

SELECTION OF THE SUCCESSFUL TENDERER

It has been requested that a short dissertation is given about the selection of the successful tenderer for a contract governed by these Conditions and about the important roles of the Engineer in this matter.

The procurement of civil engineering construction services for major projects is a matter for purchasing experts. The recommendations of FIDIC and organisations such as major petroleum companies are that four to seven selected firms of contractors – known to be capable of and interested in undertaking given major projects – are invited to tender for such projects. By so doing the choice of contractor is limited to a selection from the most economical tenders received.

Political reasons often dictate that open tenders are invited for projects without any prequalification of the tenderers. Consequently the decision to select any particular tender is influenced by the economics of the bid and the ability of the tenderer to undertake the works – taking into account his resources such as technical experience and ability, financial capacity, availability of skilled personnel and management staff and possession of or ability to acquire adequate plant and equipment.

It is therefore incumbent upon the selection committee – charged with recommending the successful tenderer – to study the details of the actual bids, to assess the proposed programmes and method statements, to identify and quantify qualifications and to assess the ability of the lowest three bidders to complete the works technically, financially within the budget and within the period of the contract.

Usually in open tendering the bidders are required to state their resources in detail as an appendix to their tender and also to provide a tender bond as "earnest" money, i.e. a token of their interest in undertaking the work. This is deemed to be a deterrent to the irresponsible contractor and to indicate that he has sufficient substance to enable him to persuade a bank to act as guarantor for the tender bond.

Later, if a bidder is selected to sign the contract he must provide a performance bond. If he cannot provide this bond, then he will not be awarded the contract and would forfeit his tender bond. This among other things calls for an absolutely impartial behaviour towards the tenderers on the part of the Employer and of his Engineer.

If tenderers believe that an Employer or an engineer is likely to betray their confidences and show partiality then they will be very reluctant to tender again for the Employer's works or for works controlled by the same Engineer.

Those responsible for procuring the best possible supplier for an Employer should encourage tenderers to disclose detailed information about their resources and technical ability to undertake the works. Similarly consulting engineers should not be prevented from calling for any information or evidence of the resources and capacity of a tenderer to enable his bid to be properly assessed in the circumstances required by the tender documents. The essential requirement is to provide the best possible deal for the ultimate purchaser of the services.

However, concerning the behaviour of a consulting engineer, it is very important that he should be very careful to treat and to be seen to treat each contractor and his tender equally in all respects. After all he is employed as a professional expert in the adjudication of the tenders and of the contractors submitting them.

He is not employed to make the choice of the successful tenderer although he will list the tenders in order of merit in accordance with the criteria set out in his terms of reference. A consulting engineer, because he is unbiased, has to be very careful to examine each tender in exactly the same way and to advise his employer precisely about the merits of and the risks in each tender.

He must assess the capability of each contractor to do the work, then appraise the amount of the offer, assess the ability of the Contractor to do the job for the amount of the offer and within the time for completion and then give a recommendation to his Employer of the merits of the bids in some order to help him select the best for his purpose.

Whereas the engineer must behave in a quasi judicial capacity in assessing the various bids he has to discriminate in order to identify the best offer for his Employer.

The following papers are recommended reading on the subject of selection:

FIDIC – *Notes on Documents for Civil Engineering Contracts*, 1977.

FIDIC – *Tendering Procedure: for obtaining and evaluating tenders for civil engineering*, 1982.

Guidance on the Preparation, Submission and Consideration of Tenders for Civil Engineering Contracts recommended for use in the United Kingdom. Institution of Civil Engineers, The Association of Consulting Engineers and The Federation of Civil Engineering Contractors, Thomas Telford, London, 1983.

8   CONCLUSION

This Digest has sought to identify the various contractual relationships and responsibilites of the Parties to the Contract and to others contributing their particular skills and expertise. Provided these are followed correctly and at the appropriate time then the Completion of the Enterprise should prove a satisfactory achievement for all involved.

However, if these relationships and responsibilities are not observed, then problems will arise which, inevitably, will get out of proportion and become extremely difficult to resolve without one Party or another involving themselves in unnecessary additional expenditure.

Problems and claims will arise during the construction of any major works but provided these are dealt with as appropriate to the circumstances, as and when they occur, then a satisfactory conclusion can be reached.

Those who use the FIDIC Conditions of Contract constantly will recognise that frequency of use provides the best way of understanding the document. The writers feel it incumbent upon themselves to remind such users that the most important feature of international construction is always to recognise the supremacy of the law of the country in which the Enterprise is being constructed.

Another important feature is the need to study very carefully all the modifications to the clauses in the document, the additional items included in Parts II and III and many other variations to the standard form which are introduced by Engineers and Employers that can change significantly the nature of the contract. Particular care is recommended when the Engineer named in Part II in the clause numbered 1 is a direct employee of the Employer.

The writers are always pleased to receive further comments on the possible modifications to the particular clauses and information about problems that have arisen during the execution of a project which bring out inadequacies and anomalies in the use of these FIDIC Conditions of Contract.

APPENDIX 1

PROJECT DIARY – AIDE MEMOIRE

This Appendix contains notes on the type of information which should be recorded by the Contractor in the Project Diary daily. The information recorded in the diaries for other Parties to the Contract may be slightly different:

External
(1) Weather during the last 24 hours actually experienced, compared with forecast plus a comment on any unusual unforeseen weather.
(2) Note any news of external affairs likely to affect project, e.g. strikes, hostilities, riots, acts of God such as earthquakes, hurricanes, landslides, and major accidents or catastrophes, unusual weather, etc., whether in the country of the project or elsewhere.

Works
(1) Work-force – numbers of various categories of staff and labour on Site for Main Contractor, Sub-Contractors, and others.
(2) List of major plant and equipment on Site – company-owned, hired and Sub-Contractor-owned.
(3) Work being undertaken that day with special reference to major pours of concrete, heavy lifts, special installations and so on.
(4) Unexpected physical conditions encountered and action taken under Clause 12.
(5) Notes on any dangerous occurrences whether or not any damage or injury resulted, and on any accidents, fires, thefts, injuries, sickness or damage to property.
(6) Note any correspondence with insurers.
(7) Notes on receipt of, and any delays experienced in, receipt of the following, including notes on news of impending delays:

    (a) materials, temporary or permanent or consumable;
    (b) plant and equipment, temporary or permanent or on hire;
    (c) drawings;
    (d) instructions;
    (e) information such as reports, test results etc.

(8) Notes on any labour unrest, strikes, rebellion, lockouts, with own and Sub-Contractors'/suppliers' work-force and with client's employees.
(9) Discussions with union officials, shop stewards and other official or unofficial spokesmen for the labour force.

Engineer
(1) Notes on any discussions with any Engineer's Representatives whether resident or visiting.
(2) Reference to receipt or despatch of key letters or notices to Engineer or his Representatives.
(3) Receipt of instructions from the Engineer or his Representative whether verbal or in writing.
(4) Despatch of written confirmation of verbal instructions.
(5) Measurement:
    (a) requests by either party to attend for measurement;
    (b) failure of either party to attend.
(6) Inspection:
    (a) requests by either party to attend inspection of ground, concrete, shuttering, reinforcement, etc.
    (b) failure to attend same.
(7) Any information about invoices, certificates and payment.

Contractors' Head Office
(1) Discussions with any officials, or visitors from Head Office.
(2) Receipt and despatch of key letters etc.
(3) Receipt of any important documents from Head Office by post, courier, telex/teleprinter.
(4) Information about invoices, certificates and payment.

Sub-Contractors and Suppliers – Nominated and Domestic
(1) Discussions with any Sub-Contractors, suppliers or services representatives whether resident or not.
(2) Receipt and despatch of key letters etc.
(3) Issue of verbal or written instructions to Sub-Contractors etc.
(4) Confirmation of verbal instructions to Sub-Contractors etc.
(5) Measurement:
    (a) requests to attend for measurement by either party;
    (b) failure to attend.
(6) Inspection:
    (a) requests to attend for inspection of work;
    (b) failure to attend.
(7) Any information about invoices, certificates and payment.

Government Officials, Client's Representatives, Bankers, etc.
(1) Discussions with any representatives of Government, client, bankers etc.
(2) Receipt and despatch of key letters etc.

Visitors to Site including Representatives of the Press, TV and Radio
(1) Notes on all visitors to Site, recording names of persons, purpose of visit and summary of activity undertaken.
(2) Notes on discussions with visitors which might have repercussions in future.

General
(1) A special marking code should be adopted to identify any event or discussion which might give rise to a claim for Extension in Time and for increased costs.
(2) If any shorthand form of notation is used then a complete legend explaining the meaning of any symbols used should be displayed prominently on the front cover of the diary.
(3) Wherever possible references should be added to identify letters, documents, drawings, plant locations, site locations, etc.
(4) In addition to any legends or reference codes used in the diary it would be useful to have a Site plan displayed as part of each volume of the Site Diary.
(5) Very important. Each page should be copied and sent to Head Office in regular and frequent batches and the original volumes must be kept in a fire-proof safe under lock and key.
(6) All diaries must be kept for at least the period stated in any relevant Act of Limitation and possibly up to fifteen years after the completion of the Contract.

APPENDIX 2

From the *FIDIC Conditions of Contract (International) for Works of Civil Engineering Construction*, 3rd Edition, March 1977.

Parts I, II and III
Form of Tender
Appendix
Form of Agreement

GENERAL CONDITIONS—Table of Contents

Conditions of Contract
PART 1 — GENERAL CONDITIONS

DEFINITIONS AND INTERPRETATION

1. (1) In the Contract, as hereinafter defined, the following words and expressions shall have the meanings hereby assigned to them, except where the context otherwise requires:— *(Definitions.)*

(a) "Employer" means the party named in Part II who will employ the Contractor and the legal successors in title to the Employer, but not, except with the consent of the Contractor, any assignee of the Employer.

(b) "Contractor" means the person or persons, firm or company whose tender has been accepted by the Employer and includes the Contractor's personal representatives, successors and permitted assigns.

(c) "Engineer" means the Engineer designated as such in Part II, or other the Engineer appointed from time to time by the Employer and notified in writing to the Contractor to act as Engineer for the purposes of the Contract in place of the Engineer so designated.

(d) "Engineer's Representative" means any resident engineer or assistant of the Engineer, or any clerk of works appointed from time to time by the Employer or the Engineer to perform the duties set forth in Clause 2 hereof, whose authority shall be notified in writing to the Contractor by the Engineer.

(e) "Works" shall include both Permanent Works and Temporary Works.

(f) "Contract" means the Conditions of Contract, Specification, Drawings, priced Bill of Quantities, Schedule of Rates and Prices, if any, Tender, Letter of Acceptance and the Contract Agreement, if completed.

(g) "Contract Price" means the sum named in the Letter of Acceptance, subject to such additions thereto or deductions therefrom as may be made under the provisions hereinafter contained.

(h) "Constructional Plant" means all appliances or things of whatsoever nature required in or about the execution or maintenance of the Works but does not include materials or other things intended to form or forming part of the Permanent Works.

(i) "Temporary Works" means all temporary works of every kind required in or about the execution or maintenance of the Works.

(j) "Permanent Works" means the permanent works to be executed and maintained in accordance with the Contract.

(k) "Specification" means the specification referred to in the Tender and any modification thereof or addition thereto as may from time to time be furnished or approved in writing by the Engineer.

(l) "Drawings" means the drawings referred to in the Specification and any modification of such drawings approved in writing by the Engineer and such other drawings as may from time to time be furnished or approved in writing by the Engineer.

(m) "Site" means the land and other places on, under, in or through which the Permanent Works or Temporary Works designed by the Engineer are to be executed and any other lands and places provided by the Employer for working space or any other purpose as may be specifically designated in the Contract as forming part of the Site.

(n) "Approved" means approved in writing, including subsequent written confirmation of previous verbal approval and "approval" means approval in writing, including as aforesaid.

(2) Words importing the singular only also include the plural and *vice versa* where the context requires. *(Singular and Plural.)*

(3) The headings and marginal notes in these Conditions of Contract shall not be deemed to be part thereof or be taken into consideration in the interpretation or construction thereof or of the Contract. *(Headings or Notes.)*

(4) The word "cost" shall be deemed to include overhead costs whether on or off the Site. *(Cost.)*

ENGINEER AND ENGINEER'S REPRESENTATIVE

2. (1) The Engineer shall carry out such duties in issuing decisions, certificates and orders as are specified in the Contract. In the event of the Engineer being required in terms of his appointment by the Employer to obtain the specific approval of the Employer for the execution of any part of these duties, this shall be set out in Part II of these Conditions. *(Duties and Powers of Engineer and Engineer's Representative.)*

(2) The Engineer's Representative shall be responsible to the Engineer and his duties are to watch and supervise the Works and to test and examine any materials to be used or workmanship employed in connection with the Works. He shall have no authority to relieve the Contractor of any of his duties or obligations under the Contract nor, except as expressly provided hereunder or elsewhere in the Contract, to order any work involving delay or any extra payment by the Employer, nor to make any variation of or in the Works.

The Engineer may from time to time in writing delegate to the Engineer's Representative any of the powers and authorities vested in the Engineer and shall furnish to the Contractor and to the Employer a copy of all such written delegations of powers and authorities. Any written instruction or approval given by the Engineer's Representative to the Contractor within the terms of such delegation, but not otherwise, shall bind the Contractor and the Employer as though it had been given by the Engineer. Provided always as follows:—

(a) Failure of the Engineer's Representative to disapprove any work or materials shall not prejudice the power of the Engineer thereafter to disapprove such work or materials and to order the pulling down, removal or breaking up thereof.

(b) If the Contractor shall be dissatisfied by reason of any decision of the Engineer's Representative he shall be entitled to refer the matter to the Engineer, who shall thereupon confirm, reverse or vary such decision.

ASSIGNMENT AND SUB-LETTING

Assignment.

3. The Contractor shall not assign the Contract or any part thereof, or any benefit or interest therein or thereunder, otherwise than by a charge in favour of the Contractor's bankers of any monies due or to become due under this Contract, without the prior written consent of the Employer.

Sub-letting.

4. The Contractor shall not sub-let the whole of the Works. Except where otherwise provided by the Contract, the Contractor shall not sub-let any part of the Works without the prior written consent of the Engineer, which shall not be unreasonably withheld, and such consent, if given, shall not relieve the Contractor from any liability or obligation under the Contract and he shall be responsible for the acts, defaults and neglects of any sub-contractor, his agents, servants or workmen as fully as if they were the acts, defaults or neglects of the Contractor, his agents, servants or workmen. Provided always that the provision of labour on a piecework basis shall not be deemed to be a sub-letting under this Clause.

CONTRACT DOCUMENTS

Language/s and Law.

5. (1) There shall be stated in Part II of these Conditions:—

(a) the language or languages in which the Contract documents shall be drawn up and

(b) the country or state, the law of which is to apply to the Contract and according to which the Contract is to be construed.

If the said documents are written in more than one language, the language according to which the Contract is to be construed and interpreted shall also be designated in Part II, being therein designated the "Ruling Language".

Documents Mutually Explanatory.

(2) Except if and to the extent otherwise provided by the Contract, the provisions of the Conditions of Contract Parts I and II shall prevail over those of any other document forming part of the Contract. Subject to the foregoing, the several documents forming the Contract are to be taken as mutually explanatory of one another, but in case of ambiguities or discrepancies the same shall be explained and adjusted by the Engineer who shall thereupon issue to the Contractor instructions thereon. Provided always that if, in the opinion of the Engineer, compliance with any such instructions shall involve the Contractor in any cost, which by reason of any such ambiguity or discrepancy could not reasonably have been foreseen by the Contractor, the Engineer shall certify and the Employer shall pay such additional sum as may be reasonable to cover such costs.

Custody of Drawings.

6. (1) The Drawings shall remain in the sole custody of the Engineer, but two copies thereof shall be furnished to the Contractor free of charge. The Contractor shall provide and make at his own expense any further copies required by him. At the completion of the Contract the Contractor shall return to the Engineer all Drawings provided under the Contract.

One Copy of Drawings to be Kept on Site.

(2) One copy of the Drawings, furnished to the Contractor as aforesaid, shall be kept by the Contractor on the Site and the same shall at all reasonable times be available for inspection and use by the Engineer and the Engineer's Representative and by any other person authorised by the Engineer in writing.

Disruption of Progress.

(3) The Contractor shall give written notice to the Engineer whenever planning or progress of the Works is likely to be delayed or disrupted unless any further drawing or order, including a direction, instruction or approval, is issued by the Engineer within a reasonable time. The notice shall include details of the drawing or order required and of why and by when it is required and of any delay or disruption likely to be suffered if it is late.

(4) If, by reason of any failure or inability of the Engineer to issue within a time reasonable in all the circumstances any drawing or order requested by the Contractor in accordance with sub-clause (3) of this Clause, the Contractor suffers delay and/or incurs costs then the Engineer shall take such delay into account in determining any extension of time to which the Contractor is entitled under Clause 44 hereof and the Contractor shall be paid the amount of such cost as shall be reasonable.

Delays and cost of delay of Drawings

7. The Engineer shall have full power and authority to supply to the Contractor from time to time, during the progress of the Works, such further drawings and instructions as shall be necessary for the purpose of the proper and adequate execution and maintenance of the Works. The Contractor shall carry out and be bound by the same.

Further Drawings and Instructions.

GENERAL OBLIGATIONS

8. (1) The Contractor shall, subject to the provisions of the Contract, and with due care and diligence, execute and maintain the Works and provide all labour, including the supervision thereof, materials, Constructional Plant and all other things, whether of a temporary or permanent nature, required in and for such execution and maintenance, so far as the necessity for providing the same is specified in or is reasonably to be inferred from the Contract.

Contractor's General Responsibilities.

(2) The Contractor shall take full responsibility for the adequacy stability and safety of all site operations and methods of construction, provided that the Contractor shall not be responsible, except as may be expressly provided in the Contract, for the design or specification of the Permanent Works, or for the design or specification of any Temporary Works prepared by the Engineer.

9. The Contractor shall when called upon so to do enter into and execute a Contract Agreement, to be prepared and completed at the cost of the Employer, in the form annexed with such modification as may be necessary.

Contract Agreement.

10. If, for the due performance of the Contract, the Tender shall contain an undertaking by the Contractor to obtain, when required, a bond or guarantee of an insurance company or bank, or other approved sureties to be jointly and severally bound with the Contractor to the Employer, in a sum not exceeding that stated in the Letter of Acceptance for such bond or guarantee, the said insurance company or bank or sureties and the terms of the said bond or guarantee shall be such as shall be approved by the Employer. The obtaining of such bond or guarantee or the provision of such sureties and the cost of the bond or guarantee to be so entered into shall be at the expense in all respects of the Contractor, unless the Contract otherwise provides.

Performance Bond.

11. The Employer shall have made available to the Contractor with the Tender documents such data on hydrological and sub-surface conditions as shall have been obtained by or on behalf of the Employer from investigations undertaken relevant to the Works and the Tender shall be deemed to have been based on such data, but the Contractor shall be responsible for his own interpretation thereof.

Inspection of Site.

The Contractor shall also be deemed to have inspected and examined the Site and its surroundings and information available in connection therewith and to have satisfied himself, so far as is practicable, before submitting his Tender, as to the form and nature thereof, including the sub-surface conditions, the hydrological and climatic conditions, the extent and nature of work and materials necessary for the completion of the Works, the means of access to the Site and the accommodation he may require and, in general, shall be deemed to have obtained all necessary information, subject as above mentioned, as to risks, contingencies and all other circumstances which may influence or affect his Tender.

12. The Contractor shall be deemed to have satisfied himself before tendering as to the correctness and sufficiency of his Tender for the Works and of the rates and prices stated in the priced Bill of Quantities and the Schedule of Rates and Prices, if any, which Tender rates and prices shall, except insofar as it is otherwise provided in the Contract, cover all his obligations under the Contract and all matters and things necessary for the proper execution and maintenance of the Works. If, however, during the execution of the Works the Contractor shall encounter physical conditions, other than climatic conditions on the Site, or artificial obstructions, which conditions or obstructions could, in his opinion, not have been reasonably foreseen by an experienced contractor, the Contractor shall forthwith give written notice thereof to the Engineer's Representative and if, in the opinion of the Engineer, such conditions or artificial obstructions could not have been reasonably foreseen by an experienced contractor, then the Engineer shall certify and the Employer shall pay the additional cost to which the Contractor shall have been put by reason of such conditions, including the proper and reasonable cost

Sufficiency of Tender.

Adverse Physical Conditions and Artificial Obstructions.

   (a) of complying with any instruction which the Engineer may issue to the Contractor in connection therewith, and

   (b) of any proper and reasonable measures approved by the Engineer which the Contractor may take in the absence of specific instructions from the Engineer,

as a result of such conditions or obstructions being encountered.

Work to be to the Satisfaction of Engineer.

13. Save insofar as it is legally or physically impossible, the Contractor shall execute and maintain the Works in strict accordance with the Contract to the satisfaction of the Engineer and shall comply with and adhere strictly to the Engineer's instructions and directions on any matter whether mentioned in the Contract or not, touching or concerning the Works. The Contractor shall take instructions and directions only from the Engineer or, subject to the limitations referred to in Clause 2 hereof, from the Engineer's Representative.

Programme to be Furnished.

14. (1) Within the time stated in Part II of these Conditions, the Contractor shall, after the acceptance of his Tender, submit to the Engineer for his approval a programme showing the order of procedure in which he proposes to carry out the Works. The Contractor shall whenever required by the Engineer or Engineers' Representative, also provide in writing for his information a general description of the arrangements and methods which the Contractor proposes to adopt for the execution of the Works.

(2) If at any time it should appear to the Engineer that the actual progress of the Works does not conform to the approved programme referred to in sub-clause (1) of this Clause, the Contractor shall produce, at the request of the Engineer, a revised programme showing the modifications to the approved programme necessary to ensure completion of the Works within the time for completion as defined in Clause 43 hereof.

(3) The submission to and approval by the Engineer or Engineer's Representative of such programmes or the furnishing of such particulars shall not relieve the Contractor of any of his duties or responsibilities under the Contract.

Contractor's Superintendence.

15. The Contractor shall give or provide all necessary superintendence during the execution of the Works and as long thereafter as the Engineer may consider necessary for the proper fulfilling of the Contractor's obligations under the Contract. The Contractor, or a competent and authorised agent or representative approved of in writing by the Engineer, which approval may at any time be withdrawn, is to be constantly on the Works and shall give his whole time to the superintendence of the same. If such approval shall be withdrawn by the Engineer, the Contractor shall, as soon as is practicable, having regard to the requirement of replacing him as hereinafter mentioned, after receiving written notice of such withdrawal, remove the agent from the Works and shall not thereafter employ him again on the Works in any capacity and shall replace him by another agent approved by the Engineer. Such authorised agent or representative shall receive, on behalf of the Contractor, directions and instructions from the Engineer or, subject to the limitations of Clause 2 hereof, the Engineer's Representative.

Contractor's Employees.

16. (1) The Contractor shall provide and employ on the Site in connection with the execution and maintenance of the Works

(a) only such technical assistants as are skilled and experienced in their respective callings and such sub-agents, foremen and leading hands as are competent to give proper supervision to the work they are required to supervise, and

(b) such skilled, semi-skilled and unskilled labour as is necessary for the proper and timely execution and maintenance of the Works.

(2) The Engineer shall be at liberty to object to and require the Contractor to remove forthwith from the Works any person employed by the Contractor in or about the execution or maintenance of the Works who, in the opinion of the Engineer, misconducts himself, or is incompetent or negligent in the proper performance of his duties, or whose employment is otherwise considered by the Engineer to be undesirable and such person shall not be again employed upon the Works without the written permission of the Engineer. Any person so removed from the Works shall be replaced as soon as possible by a competent substitute approved by the Engineer.

Setting-out.

17. The Contractor shall be responsible for the true and proper setting-out of the Works in relation to original points, lines and levels of reference given by the Engineer in writing and for the correctness, subject as above mentioned, of the position, levels, dimensions and alignment of all parts of the Works and for the provision of all necessary instruments, appliances and labour in connection therewith. If, at any time during the progress of the Works, any error shall appear or arise in the position, levels, dimensions or alignment of any part of the Works, the Contractor, on being required so to do by the Engineer or the Engineer's Representative, shall, at his own cost, rectify such error to the satisfaction of the Engineer or the Engineer's Representative, unless such error is based on incorrect data supplied in writing by the Engineer or the Engineer's Representative, in which case the expense of rectifying the same shall be borne by the Employer. The checking of any setting-out or of any line or level by the Engineer or the Engineer's Representative shall not in any way relieve the Contractor of his responsibility for the correctness thereof and the Contractor shall carefully protect and preserve all bench-marks, sight-rails, pegs and other things used in setting-out the Works.

Boreholes and Exploratory Excavation.

18. If, at any time during the execution of the Works, the Engineer shall require the Contractor to make boreholes or to carry out exploratory excavation, such requirement shall be ordered in writing and shall be deemed to be an addition ordered under the provisions of Clause 51 hereof, unless a provisional sum in respect of such anticipated work shall have been included in the Bill of Quantities.

19. The Contractor shall in connection with the Works provide and maintain at his own cost all lights, guards, fencing and watching when and where necessary or required by the Engineer or the Engineer's Representative, or by any duly constituted authority, for the protection of the Works, or for the safety and convenience of the public or others.

Watching and Lighting.

20. (1) From the commencement of the Works until the date stated in the Certificate of Completion for the whole of the Works pursuant to Clause 48 hereof the Contractor shall take full responsibility for the care thereof. Provided that if the Engineer shall issue a Certificate of Completion in respect of any part of the Permanent Works the Contractor shall cease to be liable for the care of that part of the Permanent Works from the date stated in the Certificate of Completion in respect of that part and the responsibility for the care of that part shall pass to the Employer. Provided further that the Contractor shall take full responsibility for the care of any outstanding work which he shall have undertaken to finish during the Period of Maintenance until such outstanding work is completed. In case any damage, loss or injury shall happen to the Works, or to any part thereof, from any cause whatsoever, save and except the excepted risks as defined in sub-clause (2) of this Clause, while the Contractor shall be responsible for the care thereof the Contractor shall, at his own cost, repair and make good the same, so that at completion the Permanent Works shall be in good order and condition and in conformity in every respect with the requirements of the Contract and the Engineer's instructions. In the event of any such damage, loss or injury happening from any of the excepted risks, the Contractor shall, if and to the extent required by the Engineer and subject always to the provisions of Clause 65 hereof, repair and make good the same as aforesaid at the cost of the Employer. The Contractor shall also be liable for any damage to the Works occasioned by him in the course of any operations carried out by him for the purpose of completing any outstanding work or complying with his obligations under Clauses 49 or 50 hereof.

Care of Works.

(2) The "excepted risks" are war, hostilities (whether war be declared or not), invasion, act of foreign enemies, rebellion, revolution, insurrection or military or usurped power, civil war, or unless solely restricted to employees of the Contractor or of his sub-contractors and arising from the conduct of the Works, riot, commotion or disorder, or use or occupation by the Employer of any part of the Permanent Works, or a cause solely due to the Engineer's design of the Works, or ionising radiations or contamination by radio-activity from any nuclear fuel or from any nuclear waste from the combustion of nuclear fuel, radio-active toxic explosive, or other hazardous properties of any explosive, nuclear assembly or nuclear component thereof, pressure waves caused by aircraft or other aerial devices travelling at sonic or supersonic speeds, or any such operation of the forces of nature as an experienced contractor could not foresee, or reasonably make provision for or insure against all of which are herein collectively referred to as "the excepted risks".

Excepted Risks.

21. Without limiting his obligations and responsibilities under Clause 20 hereof, the Contractor shall insure in the joint names of the Employer and the Contractor against all loss or damage from whatever cause arising, other than the excepted risks, for which he is responsible under the terms of the Contract and in such manner that the Employer and Contractor are covered for the period stipulated in Clause 20(1) hereof and are also covered during the Period of Maintenance for loss or damage arising from a cause, occurring prior to the commencement of the Period of Maintenance, and for any loss or damage occasioned by the Contractor in the course of any operations carried out by him for the purpose of complying with his obligations under Clauses 49 and 50 hereof:—

Insurance of Works, etc.

(a) The Works for the time being executed to the estimated current contract value thereof, or such additional sum as may be specified in Part II in the Clause numbered 21, together with the materials for incorporation in the Works at their replacement value.

(b) The Constructional Plant and other things brought on to the Site by the Contractor to the replacement value of such Constructional Plant and other things.

Such insurance shall be effected with an insurer and in terms approved by the Employer, which approval shall not be unreasonably withheld, and the Contractor shall, whenever required, produce to the Engineer or the Engineer's Representative the policy or policies of insurance and the receipts for payment of the current premiums.

22. (1) The Contractor shall, except if and so far as the Contract provides otherwise, indemnify the Employer against all losses and claims in respect of injuries or damage to any person or material or physical damage to any property whatsoever which may arise out of or in consequence of the execution and maintenance of the Works and against all claims, proceedings, damages, costs, charges and expenses whatsoever in respect of or in relation thereto except any compensation or damages for or with respect to:—

Damage to Persons and Property.

(a) The permanent use or occupation of land by the Works or any part thereof.

(b) The right of the Employer to execute the Works or any part thereof on, over, under, in or through any land.

(c) Injuries or damage to persons or property which are the unavoidable result of the execution or maintenance of the Works in accordance with the Contract.

(d) Injuries or damage to persons or property resulting from any act or neglect of the Employer, his agents, servants or other contractors, not being employed by the Contractor, or for or in respect of any claims, proceedings, damages, costs, charges and expenses in respect thereof or in relation thereto or where the injury or damage was contributed to by the Contractor, his servants or agents such part of the compensation as may be just and equitable having regard to the extent of the responsibility of the Employer, his servants or agents or other contractors for the damage or injury.

Indemnity by Employer.

(2) The Employer shall indemnify the Contractor against all claims, proceedings, damages, costs, charges and expenses in respect of the matters referred to in the proviso to sub-clause (1) of this Clause.

Third Party Insurance.

23.　(1) Before commencing the execution of the Works the Contractor, but without limiting his obligations and responsibilities under Clause 22 hereof, shall insure against his liability for any material or physical damage, loss or injury which may occur to any property, including that of the Employer, or to any person, including any employee of the Employer, by or arising out of the execution of the Works or in the carrying out of the Contract, otherwise than due to the matters referred to in the proviso to Clause 22 (1) hereof.

Minimum Amount of Third Party Insurance.

(2) Such insurance shall be effected with an insurer and in terms approved by the Employer, which approval shall not be unreasonably withheld, and for at least the amount stated in the Appendix to the Tender. The Contractor shall, whenever required, produce to the Engineer or the Engineer's Representative the policy or policies of insurance and the receipts for payment of the current premiums.

Provision to Indemnify Employer.

(3) The terms shall include a provision whereby, in the event of any claim in respect of which the Contractor would be entitled to receive indemnity under the policy being brought or made against the Employer, the insurer will indemnify the Employer against such claims and any costs, charges and expenses in respect thereof.

Accident or Injury to Workmen.

24.　(1) The Employer shall not be liable for or in respect of any damages or compensation payable at law in respect or in consequence of any accident or injury to any workman or other person in the employment of the Contractor or any sub-contractor, save and except an accident or injury resulting from any act or default of the Employer, his agents, or servants. The Contractor shall indemnify and keep indemnified the Employer against all such damages and compensation, save and except as aforesaid, and against all claims, proceedings, costs, charges and expenses whatsoever in respect thereof or in relation thereto.

Insurance against Accident, etc., to Workmen.

(2) The Contractor shall insure against such liability with an insurer approved by the Employer, which approval shall not be unreasonably withheld, and shall continue such insurance during the whole of the time that any persons are employed by him on the Works and shall, when required, produce to the Engineer or the Engineer's Representative such policy of insurance and the receipt for payment of the current premium. Provided always that, in respect of any persons employed by any sub-contractor, the Contractor's obligation to insure as aforesaid under this sub-clause shall be satisfied if the sub-contractor shall have insured against the liability in respect of such persons in such manner that the Employer is indemnified under the policy, but the Contractor shall require such sub-contractor to produce to the Engineer or the Engineer's Representative, when required, such policy of insurance and the receipt for the payment of the current premium.

Remedy on Contractor's Failure to Insure.

25.　If the Contractor shall fail to effect and keep in force the insurances referred to in Clauses 21, 23 and 24 hereof, or any other insurance which he may be required to effect under the terms of the Contract, then and in any such case the Employer may effect and keep in force any such insurance and pay such premium or premiums as may be necessary for that purpose and from time to time deduct the amount so paid by the Employer as aforesaid from any monies due or which may become due to the Contractor, or recover the same as a debt due from the Contractor.

Giving of Notices and Payment of Fees.

26.　(1) The Contractor shall give all notices and pay all fees required to be given or paid by any National or State Statute, Ordinance, or other Law, or any regulation, or bye-law of any local or other duly constituted authority in relation to the execution of the Works and by the rules and regulations of all public bodies and companies whose property or rights are affected or may be affected in any way by the Works.

Compliance with Statutes, Regulations, etc.

(2) The Contractor shall conform in all respects with the provisions of any such Statute, Ordinance or Law as aforesaid and the regulations or bye-laws of any local or other duly constituted authority which may be applicable to the Works and with such rules and regulations of public bodies and companies as aforesaid and shall keep the Employer indemnified against all penalties and liability of every kind for breach of any such Statute, Ordinance or Law, regulation or bye-law.

(3) The Employer will repay or allow to the Contractor all such sums as the Engineer shall certify to have been properly payable and paid by the Contractor in respect of such fees.

Fossils, etc.

27.　All fossils, coins, articles of value or antiquity and structures and other remains or things of geological or archaeological interest discovered on the site of the Works shall as between the Employer and the Contractor be deemed to be the absolute property of the Employer. The Contractor shall take reasonable precautions to prevent his workmen or any other persons from removing or damaging any such article or thing and shall immediately upon discovery thereof and, before removal, acquaint the Engineer's Representative of such discovery and carry out, at the expense of the Employer, the Engineer's Representative's orders as to the disposal of the same.

28. The Contractor shall save harmless and indemnify the Employer from and against all claims and proceedings for or on account of infringement of any patent rights, design trademark or name or other protected rights in respect of any Constructional Plant, machine work, or material used for or in connection with the Works or any of them and from and against all claims, proceedings, damages, costs, charges and expenses whatsoever in respect thereof or in relation thereto. Except where otherwise specified, the Contractor shall pay all tonnage and other royalties, rent and other payments or compensation, if any, for getting stone, sand, gravel, clay or other materials required for the Works or any of them. — **Patent Rights and Royalties.**

29. All operations necessary for the execution of the Works shall, so far as compliance with the requirements of the Contract permits, be carried on so as not to interfere unnecessarily or improperly with the convenience of the public, or the access to, use and occupation of public or private roads and footpaths to or of properties whether in the possession of the Employer or of any other person. The Contractor shall save harmless and indemnify the Employer in respect of all claims, proceedings, damages, costs, charges and expenses whatsoever arising out of, or in relation to, any such matters in so far as the Contractor is responsible therefor. — **Interference with Traffic and Adjoining Properties.**

30. (1) The Contractor shall use every reasonable means to prevent any of the highways or bridges communicating with or on the routes to the Site from being damaged or injured by any traffic of the Contractor or any of his sub-contractors and, in particular, shall select routes, choose and use vehicles and restrict and distribute loads so that any such extraordinary traffic as will inevitably arise from the moving of plant and material from and to the Site shall be limited, as far as reasonably possible, and so that no unnecessary damage or injury may be occasioned to such highways and bridges. — **Extraordinary Traffic.**

(2) Should it be found necessary for the Contractor to move one or more loads of Constructional Plant, machinery or pre-constructed units or parts of units of work over part of a highway or bridge, the moving whereof is likely to damage any highway or bridge unless special protection or strengthening is carried out, then the Contractor shall before moving the load on to such highway or bridge give notice to the Engineer or Engineer's Representative of the weight and other particulars of the load to be moved and his proposals for protecting or strengthening the said highway or bridge. Unless within fourteen days of the receipt of such notice the Engineer shall by counter-notice direct that such protection or strengthening is unnecessary, then the Contractor will carry out such proposals or any modification thereof that the Engineer shall require and, unless there is an item or are items in the Bill of Quantities for pricing by the Contractor of the necessary works for the protection or strengthening aforesaid, the costs thereof shall be paid by the Employer to the Contractor. — **Special Loads.**

(3) If during the execution of the Works or at any time thereafter the Contractor shall receive any claim arising out of the execution of the Works in respect of damage or injury to highways or bridges he shall immediately report the same to the Engineer and thereafter the Employer shall negotiate the settlement of and pay all sums due in respect of such claim and shall indemnify the Contractor in respect thereof and in respect of all claims, proceedings, damages, costs, charges and expenses in relation thereto. Provided always that if and so far as any such claims or part thereof shall in the opinion of the Engineer be due to any failure on the part of the Contractor to observe and perform his obligations under sub-clauses (1) and (2) of this Clause, then the amount certified by the Engineer to be due to such failure shall be paid by the Contractor to the Employer. — **Settlement of Extraordinary Traffic Claims.**

(4) Where the nature of the Works is such as to require the use by the Contractor of waterborne transport the foregoing provisions of this Clause shall be construed as though "highway" included a lock, dock, sea wall or other structure related to a waterway and "vehicle" included craft, and shall have effect accordingly. — **Waterborne Traffic.**

31. The Contractor shall, in accordance with the requirements of the Engineer, afford all reasonable opportunities for carrying out their work to any other contractors employed by the Employer and their workmen and to the workmen of the Employer and of any other duly constituted authorities who may be employed in the execution on or near the Site of any work not included in the Contract or of any contract which the Employer may enter into in connection with or ancillary to the Works. If, however, the Contractor shall, on the written request of the Engineer or the Engineer's Representative, make available to any such other contractor, or to the Employer or any such authority, any roads or ways for the maintenance of which the Contractor is responsible, or permit the use by any such of the Contractor's scaffolding or other plant on the Site, or provide any other service of whatsoever nature for any such, the Employer shall pay to the Contractor in respect of such use or service such sum or sums as shall, in the opinion of the Engineer, be reasonable. — **Opportunities for other Contractors.**

32. During the progress of the Works the Contractor shall keep the Site reasonably free from all unnecessary obstruction and shall store or dispose of any Constructional Plant and surplus materials and clear away and remove from the Site any wreckage, rubbish or Temporary Works no longer required. — **Contractor to Keep Site Clear.**

33. On the completion of the Works the Contractor shall clear away and remove from the Site all Constructional Plant, surplus materials, rubbish and Temporary Works of every kind, and leave the whole of the Site and Works clean and in a workmanlike condition to the satisfaction of the Engineer. — **Clearance of Site on Completion.**

LABOUR

Engagement of Labour.

34. (1) The Contractor shall make his own arrangements for the engagement of all labour, local or otherwise, and, save insofar as the Contract otherwise provides, for the transport, housing, feeding and payment thereof.

Supply of Water.

(2) The Contractor shall, so far as is reasonably practicable, having regard to local conditions, provide on the Site, to the satisfaction of the Engineer's Representative, an adequate supply of drinking and other water for the use of the Contractor's staff and work people.

Alcoholic Liquor or Drugs.

(3) The Contractor shall not, otherwise than in accordance with the Statutes, Ordinances and Government Regulations or Orders for the time being in force, import, sell, give, barter or otherwise dispose of any alcoholic liquor, or drugs, or permit or suffer any such importation, sale, gift, barter or disposal by his sub-contractors, agents or employees.

Arms and Ammunition.

(4) The Contractor shall not give, barter or otherwise dispose of to any person or persons, any arms or ammunition of any kind or permit or suffer the same as aforesaid.

Festivals and Religious Customs.

(5) The Contractor shall in all dealings with labour in his employment have due regard to all recognised festivals, days of rest and religious or other customs.

Epidemics.

(6) In the event of any outbreak of illness of an epidemic nature, the Contractor shall comply with and carry out such regulations, orders and requirements as may be made by the Government, or the local medical or sanitary authorities for the purpose of dealing with and overcoming the same.

Disorderly Conduct, etc.

(7) The Contractor shall at all times take all reasonable precautions to prevent any unlawful, riotous or disorderly conduct by or amongst his employees and for the preservation of peace and protection of persons and property in the neighbourhood of the Works against the same.

Observance by Sub-Contractors.

(8) The Contractor shall be responsible for observance by his sub-contractors of the foregoing provisions.

(9) *Any other conditions affecting labour and wages shall be as set out in Part II in the clause numbered 34 as may be necessary.*

Returns of Labour, etc.

35. The Contractor shall, if required by the Engineer, deliver to the Engineer's Representative, or at his office, a return in detail in such form and at such intervals as the Engineer may prescribe showing the supervisory staff and the numbers of the several classes of labour from time to time employed by the Contractor on the Site and such information respecting Constructional Plant as the Engineer's Representative may require.

MATERIALS AND WORKMANSHIP

Quality of Materials and Workmanship and Tests.

36. (1) All materials and workmanship shall be of the respective kinds described in the Contract and in accordance with the Engineer's instructions and shall be subjected from time to time to such tests as the Engineer may direct at the place of manufacture or fabrication, or on the Site or at such other place or places as may be specified in the Contract, or at all or any of such places. The Contractor shall provide such assistance, instruments, machines, labour and materials as are normally required for examining, measuring and testing any work and the quality, weight or quantity of any material used and shall supply samples of materials before incorporation in the Works for testing as may be slected and required by the Engineer.

Cost of Samples.

(2) All samples shall be supplied by the Contractor at his own cost if the supply thereof is clearly intended by or provided for in the Contract, but if not, then at the cost of the Employer.

Cost of Tests.

(3) The cost of making any test shall be borne by the Contractor if such test is clearly intended by or provided for in the Contract and, in the cases only of a test under load or of a test to ascertain whether the design of any finished or partially finished work is appropriate for the purposes which it was intended to fulfil, is particularised in the Contract in sufficient detail to enable the Contractor to price or allow for the same in his Tender.

Cost of Tests not Provided for, etc.

(4) If any test is ordered by the Engineer which is either

(a) not so intended by or provided for, or

(b) (in the cases above mentioned) is not so particularised, or

(c) though so intended or provided for is ordered by the Engineer to be carried out by an independent person at any place other than the Site or the place of manufacture or fabrication of the materials tested,

then the cost of such test shall be borne by the Contractor, if the test shows the workmanship or materials not to be in accordance with the provisions of the Contract or the Engineer's instructions, but otherwise by the Employer.

Inspection of Operations.

37. The Engineer and any person authorised by him shall at all times have access to the Works and to all workshops and places where work is being prepared or from where materials, manufactured articles or machinery are being obtained for the Works and the Contractor shall afford every facility for and every assistance in or in obtaining the right to such access.

38. (1) No work shall be covered up or put out of view without the approval of the Engineer or the Engineer's Representative and the Contractor shall afford full opportunity for the Engineer or the Engineer's Representative to examine and measure any work which is about to be covered up or put out of view and to examine foundations before permanent work is placed thereon. The Contractor shall give due notice to the Engineer's Representative whenever any such work or foundations is or are ready or about to be ready for examination and the Engineer's Representative shall, without unreasonable delay, unless he considers it unnecessary and advises the Contractor accordingly, attend for the purpose of examining and measuring such work or of examining such foundations.

Examination of Work before Covering up.

(2) The Contractor shall uncover any part or parts of the Works or make openings in or through the same as the Engineer may from time to time direct and shall reinstate and make good such part or parts to the satisfaction of the Engineer. If any such part or parts have been covered up or put out of view after compliance with the requirement of sub-clause (1) of this Clause and are found to be executed in accordance with the Contract, the expenses of uncovering, making openings in or through, reinstating and making good the same shall be borne by the Employer, but in any other case all costs shall be borne by the Contractor.

Uncovering and Making Openings.

39. (1) The Engineer shall during the progress of the Works have power to order in writing from time to time

Removal of Improper Work and Materials.

(a) the removal from the Site, within such time or times as may be specified in the order, of any materials which, in the opinion of the Engineer, are not in accordance with the Contract

(b) the substitution of proper and suitable materials and

(c) the removal and proper re-execution, notwithstanding any previous test thereof or interim payment therefor, of any work which in respect of materials or workmanship is not, in the opinion of the Engineer, in accordance with the Contract.

(2) In case of default on the part of the Contractor in carrying out such order, the Employer shall be entitled to employ and pay other persons to carry out the same and all expenses consequent thereon or incidental thereto shall be recoverable from the Contractor by the Employer, or may be deducted by the Employer from any monies due or which may become due to the Contractor.

Default of Contractor in Compliance.

40. (1) The Contractor shall, on the written order of the Engineer, suspend the progress of the Works or any part thereof for such time or times and in such manner as the Engineer may consider necessary and shall during such suspension properly protect and secure the work, so far as is necessary in the opinion of the Engineer. The extra cost incurred by the Contractor in giving effect to the Engineer's instructions under this Clause shall be borne and paid by the Employer unless such suspension is

Suspension of Work.

(a) otherwise provided for in the Contract, or

(b) necessary by reason of some default on the part of the Contractor, or

(c) necessary by reason of climatic conditions on the Site, or

(d) necessary for the proper execution of the Works or for the safety of the Works or any part thereof insofar as such necessity does not arise from any act or default by the Engineer or the Employer or from any of the excepted risks defined in Clause 20 hereof.

Provided that the Contractor shall not be entitled to recover any such extra cost unless he gives written notice of his intention to claim to the Engineer within twenty-eight days of the Engineer's order. The Engineer shall settle and determine such extra payment and/or extension of time under Clause 44 hereof to be made to the Contractor in respect of such claim as shall, in the opinion of the Engineer, be fair and reasonable.

(2) If the progress of the Works or any part thereof is suspended on the written order of the Engineer and if permission to resume work is not given by the Engineer within a period of ninety days from the date of suspension then, unless such suspension is within paragraph (a), (b), (c) or (d) of sub-clause (1) of this Clause, the Contractor may serve a written notice on the Engineer requiring permission within twenty-eight days from the receipt thereof to proceed with the Works, or that part thereof in regard to which progress is suspended and, if such permission is not granted within that time, the Contractor by a further written notice so served may, but is not bound to, elect or treat the suspension where it affects part only of the Works as an omission of such part under Clause 51 hereof, or, where it affects the whole Works, as an abandonment of the Contract by the Employer.

Suspension Lasting more than 90 days.

COMMENCEMENT TIME AND DELAYS

41. The Contractor shall commence the Works on Site within the period named in the Appendix to the Tender after the receipt by him of a written order to this effect from the Engineer and shall proceed with the same with due expedition and without delay, except as may be expressly sanctioned or ordered by the Engineer, or be wholly beyond the Contractor's control.

Commencement of Works.

as the Contract may prescribe, the extent of portions of the Site of which the ... n possession from time to time and the order in which such portions shall be ... and, subject to any requirement in the Contract as to the order in which the ... d, the Employer will, with the Engineer's written order to commence the ... tractor possession of so much of the Site as may be required to enable the ... ce and proceed with the execution of the Works in accordance with the ... n Clause 14 hereof, if any, and otherwise in accordance with such reasonable ... ctor as he shall, by written notice to the Engineer, make and will, from time ... roceed, give to the Contractor possession of such further portions of the Site ... enable the Contractor to proceed with the execution of the Works with due ... with the said programme or proposals, as the case may be. If the Contractor ... ost from failure on the part of the Employer to give possession in accordance ... lause, the Engineer shall grant an extension of time for the completion of the ... sum as, in his opinion, shall be fair to cover the cost incurred, which sum ... ployer.

... ctor shall bear all costs and charges for special or temporary wayleaves required by him in connection with access to the Site. The Contractor shall also provide at his own cost any additional accommodation outside the Site required by him for the purposes of the Works.

Time for Completion.

43. Subject to any requirement in the Contract as to completion of any section of the Works before completion of the whole, the whole of the Works shall be completed, in accordance with the provisions of Clause 48 hereof, within the time stated in the Contract calculated from the last day of the period named in the Appendix to the Tender as that within which the Works are to be commenced, or such extended time as may be allowed under Clause 44 hereof.

Extension of Time for Completion.

44. Should the amount of extra or additional work of any kind or any cause of delay referred to in these Conditions, or exceptional adverse climatic conditions, or other special circumstances of any kind whatsoever which may occur, other than through a default of the Contractor, be such as fairly to entitle the Contractor to an extension of time for the completion of the Works, the Engineer shall determine the amount of such extension and shall notify the Employer and the Contractor accordingly. Provided that the Engineer is not bound to take into account any extra or additional work or other special circumstances unless the Contractor has within twenty-eight days after such work has been commenced, or such circumstances have arisen, or as soon thereafter as is practicable, submitted to the Engineer's Representative full and detailed particulars of any extension of time to which he may consider himself entitled in order that such submission may be investigated at the time.

No Night or Sunday Work.

45. Subject to any provision to the contrary contained in the Contract, none of the Permanent Works shall, save as hereinafter provided, be carried on during the night or on Sundays, if locally recognised as days of rest, or their locally recognised equivalent without the permission in writing of the Engineer's Representative, except when the work is unavoidable or absolutely necessary for the saving of life or property or for the safety of the Works, in which case the Contractor shall immediately advise the Engineer's Representative. Provided always that the provisions of this Clause shall not be applicable in the case of any work which it is customary to carry out by rotary or double shifts.

Rate of Progress.

46. If for any reason, which does not entitle the Contractor to an extension of time, the rate of progress of the Works or any section is at any time, in the opinion of the Engineer, too slow to ensure completion by the prescribed time or extended time for completion, the Engineer shall so notify the Contractor in writing and the Contractor shall thereupon take such steps as are necessary and the Engineer may approve to expedite progress so as to complete the Works or such section by the prescribed time or extended time. The Contractor shall not be entitled to any additional payment for taking such steps. If, as a result of any notice given by the Engineer under this Clause, the Contractor shall seek the Engineer's permission to do any work at night or on Sundays, if locally recognised as days of rest, or their locally recognised equivalent, such permission shall not be unreasonably refused.

Liquidated Damages for Delay.

47. (1) If the Contractor shall fail to achieve completion of the Works within the time prescribed by Clause 43 hereof, then the Contractor shall pay to the Employer the sum stated in the Contract as liquidated damages for such default and not as a penalty for every day or part of a day which shall elapse between the time prescribed by Clause 43 hereof and the date of certified completion of the Works. The Employer may, without prejudice to any other method of recovery, deduct the amount of such damages from any monies in his hands, due or which may become due to the Contractor. The payment or deduction of such damages shall not relieve the Contractor from his obligation to complete the Works, or from any other of his obligations and liabilities under the Contract.

(2) If, before the completion of the whole of the Works any part or section of the Works has been certified by the Engineer as completed, pursuant to Clause 48 hereof, and occupied or used by the Employer, the liquidated damages for delay shall, for any period of delay after such certificate and in the absence of alternative provisions in the Contract be reduced in the proportion which the value of the part or section so certified bears to the value of the whole of the Works. **Reduction of Liquidated Damages.**

(3) *If it is desired to provide in the Contract for the payment of a bonus in relation to completion of the Works or of any part or section thereof this shall be set out in Part II in the clause numbered 47.* **Bonus for Completion.**

48. (1) When the whole of the Works have been substantially completed and have satisfactorily passed any final test that may be prescribed by the Contract, the Contractor may give a notice to that effect to the Engineer or to the Engineer's Representative accompanied by an undertaking to finish any outstanding work during the Period of Maintenance. Such notice and undertaking shall be in writing and shall be deemed to be a request by the Contractor for the Engineer to issue a Certificate of Completion in respect of the Works. The Engineer shall, within twenty-one days of the date of delivery of such notice either issue to the Contractor, with a copy to the Employer, a Certificate of Completion stating the date on which, in his opinion, the Works were substantially completed in accordance with the Contract or give instructions in writing to the Contractor specifying all the work which, in the Engineer's opinion, requires to be done by the Contractor before the issue of such Certificate. The Engineer shall also notify the Contractor of any defects in the Works affecting substantial completion that may appear after such instructions and before completion of the works specified therein. The Contractor shall be entitled to receive such Certificate of Completion within twenty-one days of completion to the satisfaction of the Engineer of the works so specified and making good any defects so notified. **Certification of Completion of Works.**

(2) Similarly, in accordance with the procedure set out in sub-clause (1) of this Clause, the Contractor may request and the Engineer shall issue a Certificate of Completion in respect of:— **Certification of Completion by Stages.**

(a) any section of the Permanent Works in respect of which a separate time for completion is provided in the Contract and

(b) any substantial part of the Permanent Works which has been both completed to the satisfaction of the Engineer and occupied or used by the Employer.

(3) If any part of the Permanent Works shall have been substantially completed and shall have satisfactorily passed any final test that may be prescribed by the Contract, the Engineer may issue a Certificate of Completion in respect of that part of the Permanent Works before completion of the whole of the Works and, upon the issue of such Certificate, the Contractor shall be deemed to have undertaken to complete any outstanding work in that part of the Works during the Period of Maintenance.

(4) Provided always that a Certificate of Completion given in respect of any section or part of the Permanent Works before completion of the whole shall not be deemed to certify completion of any ground or surfaces requiring reinstatement, unless such Certificate shall expressly so state.

MAINTENANCE AND DEFECTS

49. (1) In these Conditions the expression "Period of Maintenance" shall mean the period of maintenance named in the Appendix to the Tender, calculated from the date of completion of the Works, certified by the Engineer in accordance with Clause 48 hereof, or, in the event of more than one certificate having been issued by the Engineer under the said Clause, from the respective dates so certified and in relation to the Period of Maintenance the expression "the Works" shall be construed accordingly. **Definition of 'Period of Maintenance'.**

(2) To the intent that the Works shall at or as soon as practicable after the expiration of the Period of Maintenance be delivered to the Employer in the condition required by the Contract, fair wear and tear excepted, to the satisfaction of the Engineer, the Contractor shall finish the work, if any, outstanding at the date of completion, as certified under Clause 48 hereof, as soon as practicable after such date and shall execute all such work of repair, amendment, reconstruction, rectification and making good defects, imperfections, shrinkages or other faults as may be required of the Contractor in writing by the Engineer during the Period of Maintenance, or within fourteen days after its expiration, as a result of an inspection made by or on behalf of the Engineer prior to its expiration. **Execution of Work of Repair, etc.**

(3) All such work shall be carried out by the Contractor at his own expense if the necessity thereof shall, in the opinion of the Engineer, be due to the use of materials or workmanship not in accordance with the Contract, or to neglect or failure on the part of the Contractor to comply with any obligation, expressed or implied, on the Contractor's part under the Contract. If, in the opinion of the Engineer, such necessity shall be due to any other cause, the value of such work shall be ascertained and paid for as if it were additional work. **Cost of Execution of Work of Repair, etc.**

(4) If the Contractor shall fail to do any such work as aforesaid required by the Engineer, the Employer shall be entitled to employ and pay other persons to carry out the same and if such work is work which, in the opinion of the Engineer, the Contractor was liable to do at his own expense under the Contract, then all expenses consequent thereon or incidental thereto shall be recoverable from the Contractor by the Employer, or may be deducted by the Employer from any monies due or which may become due to the Contractor. **Remedy on Contractor's Failure to carry out Work Required.**

Contractor to Search.

50. The Contractor shall, if required by the Engineer in writing, search under the directions of the Engineer for the cause of any defect, imperfection or fault appearing during the progress of the Works or in the Period of Maintenance. Unless such defect, imperfection or fault shall be one for which the Contractor is liable under the Contract, the cost of the work carried out by the Contractor in searching as aforesaid shall be borne by the Employer. If such defect, imperfection or fault shall be one for which the Contractor is liable as aforesaid, the cost of the work carried out in searching as aforesaid shall be borne by the Contractor and he shall in such case repair, rectify and make good such defect, imperfection or fault at his own expense in accordance with the provisions of Clause 49 hereof.

ALTERATIONS, ADDITIONS AND OMISSIONS

Variations.

51. (1) The Engineer shall make any variation of the form, quality or quantity of the Works or any part thereof that may, in his opinion, be necessary and for that purpose, or if for any other reason it shall, in his opinion be desirable, he shall have power to order the Contractor to do and the Contractor shall do any of the following:—

(a) increase or decrease the quantity of any work included in the Contract,

(b) omit any such work,

(c) change the character or quality or kind of any such work,

(d) change the levels, lines, position and dimensions of any part of the Works, and

(e) execute additional work of any kind necessary for the completion of the Works

and no such variation shall in any way vitiate or invalidate the Contract, but the value, if any, of all such variations shall be taken into account in ascertaining the amount of the Contract Price.

Orders for Variations to be in Writing.

(2) No such variations shall be made by the Contractor without an order in writing of the Engineer. Provided that no order in writing shall be required for increase or decrease in the quantity of any work where such increase or decrease is not the result of an order given under this Clause, but is the result of the quantities exceeding or being less than those stated in the Bill of Quantities. Provided also that if for any reason the Engineer shall consider it desirable to give any such order verbally, the Contractor shall comply with such order and any confirmation in writing of such verbal order given by the Engineer, whether before or after the carrying out of the order, shall be deemed to be an order in writing within the meaning of this Clause. Provided further that if the Contractor shall within seven days confirm in writing to the Engineer and such confirmation shall not be contradicted in writing within fourteen days by the Engineer, it shall be deemed to be an order in writing by the Engineer.

Valuation of Variations.

52. (1) All extra or additional work done or work omitted by order of the Engineer shall be valued at the rates and prices set out in the Contract if, in the opinion of the Engineer, the same shall be applicable. If the Contract does not contain any rates or prices applicable to the extra or additional work, then suitable rates or prices shall be agreed upon between the Engineer and the Contractor. In the event of disagreement the Engineer shall fix such rates or prices as shall, in his opinion, be reasonable and proper.

Power of Engineer to Fix Rates.

(2) Provided that if the nature or amount of any omission or addition relative to the nature or amount of the whole of the Works or to any part thereof shall be such that, in the opinion of the Engineer, the rate or price contained in the Contract for any item of the Works is, by reason of such omission or addition, rendered unreasonable or inapplicable, then a suitable rate or price shall be agreed upon between the Engineer and the Contractor. In the event of disagreement the Engineer shall fix such other rate or price as shall, in his opinion, be reasonable and proper having regard to the circumstances.

Provided also that no increase or decrease under sub-clause (1) of this Clause or variation of rate or price under sub-clause (2) of this Clause shall be made unless, as soon after the date of the order as is practicable and, in the case of extra or additional work, before the commencement of the work or as soon thereafter as is practicable, notice shall have been given in writing:—

(a) by the Contractor to the Engineer of his intention to claim extra payment or a varied rate or price, or

(b) by the Engineer to the Contractor of his intention to vary a rate or price.

Variations Exceeding 10 per cent.

(3) If, on certified completion of the whole of the Works it shall be found that a reduction or increase greater than ten per cent of the sum named in the Letter of Acceptance, excluding all fixed sums, provisional sums and allowance for dayworks, if any, results from:—

(a) the aggregate effect of all Variation Orders, and

(b) all adjustments upon measurement of the estimated quantities set out in the Bill of Quantities, excluding all provisional sums, dayworks and adjustments of price made under Clause 70 (1) hereof,

but not from any other cause, the amount of the Contract Price shall be adjusted by such sum as may be agreed between the Contractor and the Engineer or, failing agreement, fixed by the Engineer having regard to all material and relevant factors, including the Contractor's Site and general overhead costs of the Contract.

(4) The Engineer may, if, in his opinion it is necessary or desirable, order in writing that any additional or substituted work shall be executed on a daywork basis. The Contractor shall then be paid for such work under the conditions set out in the Daywork Schedule included in the Contract and at the rates and prices affixed thereto by him in his Tender. **Daywork.**

The Contractor shall furnish to the Engineer such receipts or other vouchers as may be necessary to prove the amounts paid and, before ordering materials, shall submit to the Engineer quotations for the same for his approval.

In respect of all work executed on a daywork basis, the Contractor shall, during the continuance of such work, deliver each day to the Engineer's Representative an exact list in duplicate of the names, occupation and time of all workmen employed on such work and a statement, also in duplicate, showing the description and quantity of all materials and plant used thereon or therefor (other than plant which is included in the percentage addition in accordance with the Schedule hereinbefore referred to). One copy of each list and statement will, if correct, or when agreed, be signed by the Engineer's Representative and returned to the Contractor.

At the end of each month the Contractor shall deliver to the Engineer's Representative a priced statement of the labour, material and plant, except as aforesaid, used and the Contractor shall not be entitled to any payment unless such lists and statements have been fully and punctually rendered. Provided always that if the Engineer shall consider that for any reason the sending of such lists or statements by the Contractor, in accordance with the foregoing provision, was impracticable he shall nevertheless be entitled to authorise payment for such work, either as daywork, on being satisfied as to the time employed and plant and materials used on such work, or at such value therefor as shall, in his opinion, be fair and reasonable.

(5) The Contractor shall send to the Engineer's Representative once in every month an account giving particulars, as full and detailed as possible, of all claims for any additional payment to which the Contractor may consider himself entitled and of all extra or additional work ordered by the Engineer which he has executed during the preceding month. **Claims.**

No final or interim claim for payment for any such work or expense will be considered which has not been included in such particulars. Provided always that the Engineer shall be entitled to authorise payment to be made for any such work or expense, notwithstanding the Contractor's failure to comply with this condition, if the Contractor has, at the earliest practicable opportunity, notified the Engineer in writing that he intends to make a claim for such work.

PLANT, TEMPORARY WORKS AND MATERIALS

53.   (1) All Constructional Plant, Temporary Works and materials provided by the Contractor shall, when brought on to the Site, be deemed to be exclusively intended for the execution of the Works and the Contractor shall not remove the same or any part thereof, except for the purpose of moving it from one part of the Site to another, without the consent, in writing, of the Engineer, which shall not be unreasonably withheld. **Plant, etc.,
Exclusive Use
for the Works.**

(2) Upon completion of the Works the Contractor shall remove from the Site all the said Constructional Plant and Temporary Works remaining thereon and any unused materials provided by the Contractor. **Removal of
Plant, etc.**

(3) The Employer shall not at any time be liable for the loss of or damage to any of the said Constructional Plant, Temporary Works or materials save as mentioned in Clauses 20 and 65 hereof. **Employer not
Liable for Damage
to Plant, etc.**

(4) In respect of any Constructional Plant which the Contractor shall have imported for the purposes of the Works, the Employer will assist the Contractor, where required, in procuring any necessary Government consent to the re-export of such Constructional Plant by the Contractor upon the removal thereof as aforesaid. **Re-export
of Plant.**

(5) The Employer will assist the Contractor, where required, in obtaining clearance through the Customs of Constructional Plant, materials and other things required for the Works. **Customs
Clearance.**

(6) *Any other conditions affecting Constructional Plant, Temporary Works and materials, shall be set out in Part II in the Clause numbered 53 as may be necessary.*

54.   The operation of Clause 53 hereof shall not be deemed to imply any approval by the Engineer of the materials or other matters referred to therein nor shall it prevent the rejection of any such materials at any time by the Engineer. **Approval of
Materials, etc.,
not implied.**

MEASUREMENT

55.   The quantities set out in the Bill of Quantities are the estimated quantities of the work, but they are not to be taken as the actual and correct quantities of the Works to be executed by the Contractor in fulfilment of his obligations under the Contract. **Quantities.**

Works to be Measured.

56. The Engineer shall, except as otherwise stated, ascertain and determine by measurement the value in terms of the Contract of work done in accordance with the Contract. He shall, when he requires any part or parts of the Works to be measured, give notice to the Contractor's authorised agent or representative, who shall forthwith attend or send a qualified agent to assist the Engineer or the Engineer's Representative in making such measurement, and shall furnish all particulars required by either of them. Should the Contractor not attend, or neglect or omit to send such agent, then the measurement made by the Engineer or approved by him shall be taken to be the correct measurement of the work. For the purpose of measuring such permanent work as is to be measured by records and drawings, the Engineer's Representative shall prepare records and drawings month by month of such work and the Contractor, as and when called upon to do so in writing, shall, within fourteen days, attend to examine and agree such records and drawings with the Engineer's Representative and shall sign the same when so agreed. If the Contractor does not so attend to examine and agree such records and drawings, they shall be taken to be correct. If, after examination of such records and drawings, the Contractor does not agree the same or does not sign the same as agreed, they shall nevertheless be taken to be correct, unless the Contractor shall, within fourteen days of such examination, lodge with the Engineer's Representative, for decision by the Engineer, notice in writing of the respects in which such records and drawings are claimed by him to be incorrect.

Method of Measurement.

57. The Works shall be measured net, notwithstanding any general or local custom, except where otherwise specifically described or prescribed in the Contract.

PROVISIONAL SUMS

Definition of "Provisional Sums."

58. (1) "Provisional Sum" means a sum included in the Contract and so designated in the Bill of Quantities for the execution of work or the supply of goods, materials, or services, or for contingencies, which sum may be used, in whole or in part, or not at all, at the direction and discretion of the Engineer. The Contract Price shall include only such amounts in respect of the work, supply or services to which such Provisional Sums relate as the Engineer shall approve or determine in accordance with this Clause.

Use of Provisional Sums.

(2) In respect of every Provisional Sum the Engineer shall have power to order:—

(a) Work to be executed, including goods, materials or services to be supplied by the Contractor. The Contract Price shall include the value of such work executed or such goods, materials or services supplied determined in accordance with Clause 52 hereof

(b) Work to be executed or goods, materials or services to be supplied by a nominated Sub-Contractor as hereinafter defined. The sum to be paid to the Contractor therefor shall be determined and paid in accordance with Clause 59 (4) hereof.

(c) Goods and materials to be purchased by the Contractor. The sum to be paid to the Contractor therefor shall be determined and paid in accordance with Clause 59 (4) hereof.

Production of Vouchers, etc.

(3) The Contractor shall, when required by the Engineer, produce all quotations, invoices, vouchers and accounts or receipts in connection with expenditure in respect of Provisional Sums.

NOMINATED SUB-CONTRACTORS

Definition of "Nominated Sub-Contractors."

59. (1) All specialists, merchants, tradesmen and others executing any work or supplying any goods, materials or services for which Provisional Sums are included in the Contract, who may have been or be nominated or selected or approved by the Employer or the Engineer, and all persons to whom by virtue of the provisions of the Contract the Contractor is required to sub-let any work shall, in the execution of such work or the supply of such goods, materials or services, be deemed to be sub-contractors employed by the Contractor and are referred to in this Contract as "nominated Sub-Contractors".

Nominated Sub-Contractors; Objection to Nomination.

(2) The Contractor shall not be required by the Employer or the Engineer or be deemed to be under any obligation to employ any nominated Sub-Contractor against whom the Contractor may raise reasonable objection, or who shall decline to enter into a sub-contract with the Contractor containing provisions:—

(a) that in respect of the work, goods, materials or services the subject of the sub-contract, the nominated Sub-Contractor will undertake towards the Contractor the like obligations and liabilities as are imposed on the Contractor towards the Employer by the terms of the Contract and will save harmless and indemnify the Contractor from and against the same and from all claims, proceedings, damages, costs, charges and expenses whatsoever arising out of or in connection therewith, or arising out of or in connection with any failure to perform such obligations or to fulfil such liabilities, and

(b) that the nominated Sub-Contractor will save harmless and indemnify the Contractor from and against any negligence by the nominated Sub-Contractor, his agents, workmen and servants and from and against any misuse by him or them of any Constructional Plant or Temporary Works provided by the Contractor for the purposes of the Contract and from all claims as aforesaid.

(3) If in connection with any Provisional Sum the services to be provided include any matter of design or specification of any part of the Permanent Works or of any equipment or plant to be incorporated therein, such requirement shall be expressly stated in the Contract and shall be included in any nominated Sub-Contract. The nominated Sub-Contract shall specify that the nominated Sub-Contractor providing such services will save harmless and indemnify the Contractor from and against the same and from all claims, proceedings, damages, costs, charges and expenses whatsoever arising out of or in connection with any failure to perform such obligations or to fulfil such liabilities. **Design Requirements to be Expressly Stated.**

(4) For all work executed or goods, materials, or services supplied by any nominated Sub-Contractor, there shall be included in the Contract Price:— **Payments to Nominated Sub-Contractors.**

(a) the actual price paid or due to be paid by the Contractor, on the direction of the Engineer, and in accordance with the Sub-Contract;

(b) the sum, if any, entered in the Bill of Quantities for labour supplied by the Contractor in connection therewith, or if ordered by the Engineer pursuant to Clause 58 (2) (b) hereof, as may be determined in accordance with Clause 52 hereof;

(c) in respect of all other charges and profit, a sum being a percentage rate of the actual price paid or due to be paid calculated, where provision has been made in the Bill of Quantities for a rate to be set against the relevant Provisional Sum, at the rate inserted by the Contractor against that item or, where no such provision has been made, at the rate inserted by the Contractor in the Appendix to the Tender and repeated where provision for such is made in a special item provided in the Bill of Quantities for such purpose.

(5) Before issuing, under Clause 60 hereof, any certificate, which includes any payment in respect of work done or goods, materials or services supplied by any nominated Sub-Contractor, the Engineer shall be entitled to demand from the Contractor reasonable proof that all payments, less retentions, included in previous certificates in respect of the work or goods, materials or services of such nominated Sub-Contractor have been paid or discharged by the Contractor, in default whereof unless the Contractor shall **Certification of Payments to Nominated Sub-Contractors.**

(a) inform the Engineer in writing that he has reasonable cause for withholding or refusing to make such payments and

(b) produce to the Engineer reasonable proof that he has so informed such nominated Sub-Contractor in writing,

the Employer shall be entitled to pay to such nominated Sub-Contractor direct, upon the certificate of the Engineer, all payments, less retentions, provided for in the Sub-Contract, which the Contractor has failed to make to such nominated Sub-Contractor and to deduct by way of set-off the amount so paid by the Employer from any sums due or which may become due from the Employer to the Contractor.

Provided always that, where the Engineer has certified and the Employer has paid direct as aforesaid, the Engineer shall in issuing any further certificate in favour of the Contractor deduct from the amount thereof the amount so paid, direct as aforesaid, but shall not withhold or delay the issue of the certificate itself when due to be issued under the terms of the Contract.

(6) In the event of a nominated Sub-Contractor, as hereinbefore defined, having undertaken towards the Contractor in respect of the work executed, or the goods, materials or services supplied by such nominated Sub-Contractor, any continuing obligation extending for a period exceeding that of the Period of Maintenance under the Contract, the Contractor shall at any time, after the expiration of the Period of Maintenance, assign to the Employer, at the Employer's request and cost, the benefit of such obligation for the unexpired duration thereof. **Assignment of Nominated Sub-Contractors' Obligations.**

CERTIFICATES AND PAYMENT

60. (1) Unless otherwise provided, payments shall be made at monthly intervals in accordance with the conditions set out in Part II in the Clause numbered 60. **Certificates and Payment.**

(2) *Where advances are to be made by the Employer to the Contractor in respect of Constructional Plant and materials, the conditions of payment and repayment shall be as set out in Part II in the Clause numbered 60.* **Advances on Constructional Plant and Materials**

(3) If the execution of the Works shall necessitate the importation of materials, plant or equipment from a country other than that in which the Works are being executed, or if the Works or any part thereof are to be executed by labour imported from any other such country, or if any other circumstances shall render it necessary or desirable, a proportion of the payments to be made under the Contract shall be made in the appropriate foreign currencies and in accordance with the provisions of Clause 72 hereof. The conditions under which such payments are to be made shall be as set out in Part II in the Clause numbered 60. **Payment in Foreign Currencies.**

61. No certificate other than the Maintenance Certificate referred to in Clause 62 hereof shall be deemed to constitute approval of the Works. **Approval only by Maintenance Certificate.**

62. (1) The Contract shall not be considered as completed until a Maintenance Certificate shall have been signed by the Engineer and delivered to the Employer stating that the Works have been completed and maintained to his satisfaction. The Maintenance Certificate shall be given by the **Maintenance Certificate.**

Engineer within twenty-eight days after the expiration of the Period of Maintenance, or, if different periods of maintenance shall become applicable to different sections or parts of the Works, the expiration of the latest such period, or as soon thereafter as any works ordered during such period, pursuant to Clauses 49 and 50 hereof, shall have been completed to the satisfaction of the Engineer and full effect shall be given to this Clause, notwithstanding any previous entry on the Works or the taking possession, working or using thereof or any part thereof by the Employer. Provided always that the issue of the Maintenance Certificate shall not be a condition precedent to payment to the Contractor of the second portion of the retention money in accordance with the conditions set out in Part II in the Clause numbered 60.

Cessation of Employer's Liability.

(2) The Employer shall not be liable to the Contractor for any matter or thing arising out of or in connection with the Contract or the execution of the Works, unless the Contractor shall have made a claim in writing in respect thereof before the giving of the Maintenance Certificate under this Clause.

Unfulfilled Obligations.

(3) Notwithstanding the issue of the Maintenance Certificate the Contractor and, subject to sub-clause (2) of this Clause, the Employer shall remain liable for the fulfilment of any obligation incurred under the provisions of the Contract prior to the issue of the Maintenance Certificate which remains unperformed at the time such Certificate is issued and, for the purposes of determining the nature and extent of any such obligation, the Contract shall be deemed to remain in force between the parties hereto.

REMEDIES AND POWERS

Default of Contractor.

63. (1) If the Contractor shall become bankrupt, or have a receiving order made against him, or shall present his petition in bankruptcy, or shall make an arrangement with or assignment in favour of his creditors, or shall agree to carry out the Contract under a committee of inspection of his creditors or, being a corporation, shall go into liquidation (other than a voluntary liquidation for the purposes of amalgamation or reconstruction), or if the Contractor shall assign the Contract, without the consent in writing of the Employer first obtained, or shall have an execution levied on his goods, or if the Engineer shall certify in writing to the Employer that in his opinion the Contractor:—

(a) has abandoned the Contract, or

(b) without reasonable excuse has failed to commence the Works or has suspended the progress of the Works for twenty-eight days after receiving from the Engineer written notice to proceed, or

(c) has failed to remove materials from the Site or to pull down and replace work for twenty-eight days after receiving from the Engineer written notice that the said materials or work had been condemned and rejected by the Engineer under these conditions, or

(d) despite previous warnings by the Engineer, in writing, is not executing the Works in accordance with the Contract, or is persistently or flagrantly neglecting to carry out his obligations under the Contract, or

(e) has, to the detriment of good workmanship, or in defiance of the Engineer's instructions to the contrary, sub-let any part of the Contract

then the Employer may, after giving fourteen days' notice in writing to the Contractor, enter upon the Site and the Works and expel the Contractor therefrom without thereby voiding the Contract, or releasing the Contractor from any of his obligations or liabilities under the Contract, or affecting the rights and powers conferred on the Employer or the Engineer by the Contract, and may himself complete the Works or may employ any other contractor to complete the Works. The Employer or such other contractor may use for such completion so much of the Constructional Plant, Temporary Works and materials, which have been deemed to be reserved exclusively for the execution of the Works, under the provisions of the Contract, as he or they may think proper, and the Employer may, at any time, sell any of the said Constructional Plant, Temporary Works and unused materials and apply the proceeds of sale in or towards the satisfaction of any sums due or which may become due to him from the Contractor under the Contract.

Valuation at Date of Forfeiture.

(2) The Engineer shall, as soon as may be practicable after any such entry and expulsion by the Employer, fix and determine *ex parte*, or by or after reference to the parties, or after such investigation or enquiries as he may think fit to make or institute, and shall certify what amount, if any, had at the time of such entry and expulsion been reasonably earned by or would reasonably accrue to the Contractor in respect of work then actually done by him under the Contract and the value of any of the said unused or partially used materials, any Constructional Plant and any Temporary Works.

Payment after Forfeiture.

(3) If the Employer shall enter and expel the Contractor under this Clause, he shall not be liable to pay to the Contractor any money on account of the Contract until the expiration of the Period of Maintenance and thereafter until the costs of execution and maintenance, damages for delay in completion, if any, and all other expenses incurred by the Employer have been ascertained and the amount thereof certified by the Engineer. The Contractor shall then be entitled to receive only such sum or sums, if any, as the Engineer may certify would have been payable to him upon due

completion by him after deducting the said amount. If such amount shall exceed the sum which would have been payable to the Contractor on due completion by him, then the Contractor shall, upon demand, pay to the Employer the amount of such excess and it shall be deemed a debt due by the Contractor to the Employer and shall be recoverable accordingly.

64. If, by reason of any accident, or failure, or other event occurring to in or in connection with the Works, or any part thereof, either during the execution of the Works, or during the Period of Maintenance, any remedial or other work or repair shall, in the opinion of the Engineer or the Engineer's Representative, be urgently necessary for the safety of the Works and the Contractor is unable or unwilling at once to do such work or repair, the Employer may employ and pay other persons to carry out such work or repair as the Engineer or the Engineer's Representative may consider necessary. If the work or repair so done by the Employer is work which, in the opinion of the Engineer, the Contractor was liable to do at his own expense under the Contract, all expenses properly incurred by the Employer in so doing shall be recoverable from the Contractor by the Employer, or may be deducted by the Employer from any monies due or which may become due to the Contractor. Provided always that the Engineer or the Engineer's Representative, as the case may be, shall, as soon after the occurrence of any such emergency as may be reasonably practicable, notify the Contractor thereof in writing.

Urgent Repairs.

SPECIAL RISKS

65. Notwithstanding anything in the Contract contained:—

(1) The Contractor shall be under no liability whatsoever whether by way of indemnity or otherwise for or in respect of destruction of or damage to the Works, save to work condemned under the provisions of Clause 39 hereof prior to the occurrence of any special risk hereinafter mentioned, or to property whether of the Employer or third parties, or for or in respect of injury or loss of life which is the consequence of any special risk as hereinafter defined. The Employer shall indemnify and save harmless the Contractor against and from the same and against and from all claims, proceedings, damages, costs, charges and expenses whatsoever arising thereout or in connection therewith.

No Liability for War, etc., Risks.

(2) If the Works or any materials on or near or in transit to the Site, or any other property of the Contractor used or intended to be used for the purposes of the Works, shall sustain destruction or damage by reason of any of the said special risks the Contractor shall be entitled to payment for:—

Damage to Works, etc., by Special Risks.

(a) any permanent work and for any materials so destroyed or damaged,

and, so far as may be required by the Engineer, or as may be necessary for the completion of the Works, on the basis of cost plus such profit as the Engineer may certify to be reasonable;

(b) replacing or making good any such destruction or damage to the Works;

(c) replacing or making good such materials or other property of the Contractor used or intended to be used for the purposes of the Works.

(3) Destruction, damage, injury or loss of life caused by the explosion or impact whenever and wherever occurring of any mine, bomb, shell, grenade, or other projectile, missile, munition, or explosive of war, shall be deemed to be a consequence of the said special risks.

Projectile, Missile, etc.

(4) The Employer shall repay to the Contractor any increased cost of or incidental to the execution of the Works, other than such as may be attributable to the cost of reconstructing work condemned under the provisions of Clause 39 hereof, prior to the occurrence of any special risk, which is howsoever attributable to or consequent on or the result of or in any way whatsoever connected with the said special risks, subject however to the provisions in this Clause hereinafter contained in regard to outbreak of war, but the Contractor shall as soon as any such increase of cost shall come to his knowledge forthwith notify the Engineer thereof in writing.

Increased Costs arising from Special Risks.

(5) The special risks are war, hostilities (whether war be declared or not), invasion, act of foreign enemies, the nuclear and pressurewaves risk described in Clause 20 (2) hereof, or insofar as it relates to the country in which the Works are being or are to be executed or maintained, rebellion, revolution, insurrection, military or usurped power, civil war, or, unless solely restricted to the employees of the Contractor or of his Sub-Contractors and arising from the conduct of the Works, riot, commotion or disorder.

Special Risks.

(6) If, during the currency of the Contract, there shall be an outbreak of war, whether war is declared or not, in any part of the world which, whether financially or otherwise, materially affects the execution of the Works, the Contractor shall, unless and until the Contract is terminated under the provisions of this Clause, continue to use his best endeavours to complete the execution of the Works. Provided always that the Employer shall be entitled at any time after such outbreak of war to terminate the Contract by giving written notice to the Contractor and, upon such notice being given, this Contract shall, except as to the rights of the parties under this Clause and to the operation of Clause 67 hereof, terminate, but without prejudice to the rights of either party in respect of any antecedent breach thereof.

Outbreak of War.

Removal of Plant on Termination.

(7) If the Contract shall be terminated under the provisions of the last preceding sub-clause, the Contractor shall, with all reasonable despatch, remove from the Site all Constructional Plant and shall give similar facilities to his Sub-Contractors to do so.

Payment if Contract Terminated.

(8) If the Contract shall be terminated as aforesaid, the Contractor shall be paid by the Employer, insofar as such amounts or items shall not have already been covered by payments on account made to the Contractor, for all work executed prior to the date of termination at the rates and prices provided in the Contract and in addition:—

(a) The amounts payable in respect of any preliminary items, so far as the work or service comprised therein has been carried out or performed, and a proper proportion as certified by the Engineer of any such items, the work or service comprised in which has been partially carried out or performed.

(b) The cost of materials or goods reasonably ordered for the Works which shall have been delivered to the Contractor or of which the Contractor is legally liable to accept delivery, such materials or goods becoming the property of the Employer upon such payments being made by him.

(c) A sum to be certified by the Engineer, being the amount of any expenditure reasonably incurred by the Contractor in the expectation of completing the whole of the Works insofar as such expenditure shall not have been covered by the payments in this sub-clause before mentioned.

(d) Any additional sum payable under the provisions of sub-clauses (1), (2) and (4) of this Clause.

(e) The reasonable cost of removal of Constructional Plant under sub-clause (7) of this Clause and, if required by the Contractor, return thereof to the Contractor's main plant yard in his country of registration or to other destination, at no greater cost.

(f) The reasonable cost of repatriation of all the Contractor's staff and workmen employed on or in connection with the Works at the time of such termination.

Provided always that against any payments due from the Employer under this sub-clause, the Employer shall be entitled to be credited with any outstanding balances due from the Contractor for advances in respect of Constructional Plant and materials and any other sums which at the date of termination were recoverable by the Employer from the Contractor under the terms of the Contract.

FRUSTRATION

Payment in Event of Frustration.

66. If a war, or other circumstances outside the control of both parties, arises after the Contract is made so that either party is prevented from fulfilling his contractual obligations, or under the law governing the Contract, the parties are released from further performance, then the sum payable by the Employer to the Contractor in respect of the work executed shall be the same as that which would have been payable under Clause 65 hereof if the Contract had been terminated under the provisions of Clause 65 hereof.

SETTLEMENT OF DISPUTES

Settlement of Disputes— Arbitration.

67. If any dispute or difference of any kind whatsoever shall arise between the Employer and the Contractor or the Engineer and the Contractor in connection with, or arising out of the Contract, or the execution of the Works, whether during the progress of the Works or after their completion and whether before or after the termination, abandonment or breach of the Contract, it shall, in the first place, be referred to and settled by the Engineer who shall, within a period of ninety days after being requested by either party to do so, give written notice of his decision to the Employer and the Contractor. Subject to arbitration, as hereinafter provided, such decision in respect of every matter so referred shall be final and binding upon the Employer and the Contractor and shall forthwith be given effect to by the Employer and by the Contractor, who shall proceed with the execution of the Works with all due diligence whether he or the Employer requires arbitration, as hereinafter provided, or not. If the Engineer has given written notice of his decision to the Employer and the Contractor and no claim to arbitration has been communicated to him by either the Employer or the Contractor within a period of ninety days from receipt of such notice, the said decision shall remain final and binding upon the Employer and the Contractor. If the Engineer shall fail to give notice of his decision, as aforesaid, within a period of ninety days after being requested as aforesaid, or if either the Employer or the Contractor be dissatisfied with any such decision, then and in any such case either the Employer or the Contractor may within ninety days after receiving notice of such decision, or within ninety days after the expiration of the first-named period of ninety days, as the case may be, require that the matter or matters in dispute be referred to arbitration as hereinafter provided. All disputes or differences in respect of which the decision, if any, of the Engineer has not become final and binding as aforesaid shall be finally settled under the Rules of Conciliation and Arbitration of the International Chamber of Commerce by one or more arbitrators appointed under such Rules. The said arbitrator/s shall have full power to open up, revise and review any decision, opinion, direction, certificate or valuation of the Engineer. Neither party shall be limited in the proceedings before such arbitrator/s to the evidence or arguments put before the Engineer for the purpose of obtaining his said decision. No decision given by the Engineer in accordance with the foregoing provisions shall disqualify him from being called as a witness and giving evidence before the arbitrator/s on any matter whatsoever relevant to the dispute or difference referred to the arbitrator/s as aforesaid. The reference to arbitration may proceed notwithstanding that the Works shall not then be or be alleged to be complete, provided always that the obligations of the Employer, the Engineer and the Contractor shall not be altered by reason of the arbitration being conducted during the progress of the Works.

NOTICES

68.   (1) All certificates, notices or written orders to be given by the Employer or by the Engineer to the Contractor under the terms of the Contract shall be served by sending by post to or delivering the same to the Contractor's principal place of business, or such other address as the Contractor shall nominate for this purpose. *(Service of Notices on Contractor.)*

(2) All notices to be given to the Employer or to the Engineer under the terms of the Contract shall be served by sending by post or delivering the same to the respective addresses nominated for that purpose in Part II of these Conditions. *(Service of Notices on Employer or Engineer.)*

(3) Either party may change a nominated address to another address in the country where the Works are being executed by prior written notice to the other party and the Engineer may do so by prior written notice to both parties. *(Change of Address.)*

DEFAULT OF EMPLOYER

69.   (1) In the event of the Employer:— *(Default of Employer.)*

(a) failing to pay to the Contractor the amount due under any certificate of the Engineer within thirty days after the same shall have become due under the terms of the Contract, subject to any deduction that the Employer is entitled to make under the Contract, or

(b) interfering with or obstructing or refusing any required approval to the issue of any such certificate, or

(c) becoming bankrupt or, being a company, going into liquidation, other than for the purpose of a scheme of reconstruction or amalgamation, or

(d) giving formal notice to the Contractor that for unforeseen reasons, due to economic dislocation, it is impossible for him to continue to meet his contractual obligations

the Contractor shall be entitled to terminate his employment under the Contract after giving fourteen days' prior written notice to the Employer, with a copy to the Engineer.

(2) Upon the expiry of the fourteen days' notice referred to in sub-clause (1) of this Clause, the Contractor shall, notwithstanding the provisions of Clause 53 (1) hereof, with all reasonable despatch, remove from the Site all Constructional Plant brought by him thereon.

(3) In the event of such termination the Employer shall be under the same obligations to the Contractor in regard to payment as if the Contract had been terminated under the provisions of Clause 65 hereof, but, in addition to the payments specified in Clause 65 (8) hereof, the Employer shall pay to the Contractor the amount of any loss or damage to the Contractor arising out of or in connection with or by consequence of such termination.

CHANGES IN COSTS AND LEGISLATION

70.   (1) Adjustments to the Contract Price shall be made in respect of rise or fall in the costs of labour and/or materials or any other matters affecting the cost of the execution of the Works, as set out in Part II in the Clause numbered 70. *(Increase or Decrease of Costs.)*

(2) If, after the date thirty days prior to the latest date for submission of tenders for the Works there occur in the country in which the Works are being or are to be executed changes to any National or State Statute, Ordinance, Decree or other Law or any regulation or bye-law of any local or other duly constituted authority, or the introduction of any such State Statute, Ordinance, Decree, Law, regulation or bye-law which causes additional or reduced cost to the Contractor, other than under sub-clause (1) of this Clause, in the execution of the Works, such additional or reduced cost shall be certified by the Engineer and shall be paid by or credited to the Employer and the Contract Price adjusted accordingly. *(Subsequent Legislation.)*

CURRENCY AND RATES OF EXCHANGE

71.   If, after the date thirty days prior to the latest date for submission of tenders for the Works the Government or authorised agency of the Government of the country in which the Works are being or are to be executed imposes currency restrictions and/or transfer of currency restrictions in relation to the currency or currencies in which the Contract Price is to be paid, the Employer shall *(Currency Restrictions.)*

reimburse any loss or damage to the Contractor arising therefrom, without prejudice to the right of the Contractor to exercise any other rights or remedies to which he is entitled in such event.

Rates of Exchange

72. (1) Where the Contract provides for payment in whole or in part to be made to the Contractor in foreign currency or currencies, such payment shall not be subject to variations in the rate or rates of exchange between such specified foreign currency or currencies and the currency of the country in which the Works are to be executed.

(2) Where the Employer shall have required the Tender to be expressed in a single currency but with payment to be made in more than one currency and the Contractor has stated the proportions or amounts of other currency or currencies in which he requires payment to be made, the rate or rates of exchange applicable for calculating the payment of such proportions or amounts shall be those prevailing, as determined by the Central Bank of the country in which the Works are to be executed, on the date thirty days prior to the latest date for the submission of tenders for the Works, as shall have been notified to the Contractor by the Employer prior to the submission of tenders or as provided for in the tender documents.

(3) Where the Contract provides for payment in more than one currency, the proportions or amounts to be paid in foreign currencies in respect of Provisional Sum items shall be determined in accordance with the principles set forth in sub-clauses (1) and (2) of this Clause as and when these sums are utilised in whole or in part in accordance with the provisions of Clauses 58 and 59 hereof.

NOTE

FOR CONDITIONS OF PARTICULAR APPLICATION—SEE PART II

FOR CONDITIONS OF PARTICULAR APPLICATION TO DREDGING AND RECLAMATION WORK
—SEE PART III

Conditions of Contract
PART II—CONDITIONS OF PARTICULAR APPLICATION

The following notes are intended as an aide-memoire in the preparation of clauses (some of which are dealt with but not exhaustively in Part I) which will vary as necessary to take account of the circumstances and locality of the Works. These variable clauses which must be specially prepared to suit each particular contract should cover such of the under-mentioned matters and any others as are applicable.

Clause 1—Definitions
Employer: The Employer is ....
Engineer: The Engineer is ....
Further definitions as necessary.

Clause 2—Powers and Duties of Engineer.
Define Clauses under which specific approval of the Employer is required.

Clause 5—Language/s and Law
The language is/are ....
The Ruling Language is...
The Law to which the Contract is to be subject is...

Clause 8—Contractor's General Responsibilities
Employment of local personnel and purchase of local supplies.

Clause 10—Performance Bond
Form and percentage of Performance Bond (if required). Time limit for submission.

Clause 14—Programme
Time limit for submission of programme.

Clause 15—Contractor's Superintendence
Languages to be spoken by Contractor's Agent; registration of expatriate personnel.

Clause 16—Contractor's Employees
Languages to be spoken by other members of Contractor's staff; employment of locally recruited staff; currency of payments to Contractor's Site staff.

Clause 21—Insurance of Works
Availability of insurance cover note before work commences. Use of local insurance companies; notification by Contractor of changes in the nature or extent of the Works. Additional insurance of Works as required in special circumstances.

Clause 24—Accident or Injury to Workmen
Payments (if any) to be made as dues to a State organisation in respect of Employer's liability, in relation to Contractor's responsibilities under Clause 24 (2).

Clause 34—Labour
Permits and registration of expatriate employees; repatriation to place of recruitment; provision of temporary housing for employees; requirements in respect of accommodation for staff of Employer and Engineer; standards of accommodation to be provided; provision of access roads, hospital, school, power, water, drainage, fire services, refuse collection, communal buildings, shops, telephones; hours and conditions of working; rates of pay; compliance with labour legislation; maintenance of records of safety and health.

NOTE: Full details to be included in the Specification.

Clause 36—Quality of Materials
Utilisation of local materials.

Clause 43—Time for Completion
Reference to completion by stages, if required.

Clause 45—Night or Sunday
Reference to any special requirements to working by night or on locally recognised holidays.

Clause 47—Bonus and Liquidated Damages
Bonus (if any) for achievement of target date; if none, insert "Nil" in Appendix to the Tender; details of both liquidated damages and bonus (if any) to be included in the Specification including relation to interim dates; in the case of liquidated damages, calculation of amount, method of deducting, upper limit, currency, reduction as work is substantially completed; in the case of bonus, currency of payments.

Clause 49—Maintenance and Defects
In appropriate cases, where the permanent reinstatement is not being carried out by the Contractor, an additional sub-clause should be added to Clause 49 to cover making good all subsidence, etc. in the temporary reinstatement of any highway broken into for the purposes of the execution of the Works and the liability for damage and injury resulting therefrom up to the end of the Period of Maintenance or until possession of the Site has been taken for the purpose of carrying out permanent reinstatement (whichever is the earlier).

Clause 53—Plant

Hire of plant, sale or disposal of plant, payment of or relief from Customs or other import duties, harbour and port dues, wharfage, landing, pilotage and any other charges or dues, any other conditions affecting plant. Define, if used, "Hired Plant", "Essential Hired Plant", "Hire Purchase", "Agreement to Hire", "Ownership". Exclude from the provisions of Clause 53, any vehicles engaged in the transport of labour, plant, equipment or materials to and from the Site.

Clause 59—Nominated Sub-Contractors

Provisions for design by Nominated Sub-Contractor (if any).

Clause 60—Certificates and Payments

Advances on plant and materials where made, conditions covering such advances and their repayment; monthly claims for work executed and certificates of Engineer as to amount due to Contractor for permanent work executed in the month and for temporary works included in the Bill of Quantities and also, if there are no advances for materials and plant amounts, as certified by the Engineer for any materials for permanent work on the Site.

Arrangements for deduction and subsequent release of Retention Money, Percentage and limit of Retention as in Appendix to the Tender.

Correction and withholding of certificates; place of payment; frequency of payment (if not monthly). Minimum amount of Interim Certificates and time within which payments to be made after the issue of the Certificate, as in Appendix to the Tender.

Currency or currencies, proportions of various currencies, rates of exchange and conditions applicable thereto, in and under which payments and/or deductions are to be made, to be included in Clause 60 or, if not to be predetermined, to be as inserted by the Contractor in the Tender, for approval by the Employer and inclusion in the Contract as an Appendix to the Bill of Quantities.

As it is desirable to have all financial matters settled as soon as practicable after completion of a contract, it is suggested that the following or equivalent paragraph be included in Clause 60:—

"Not later than . . . months after the issue of the Maintenance Certificate the Contractor shall submit to the Engineer a statement of final account with supporting documents showing in detail the value of the work done in accordance with the Contract together with all further sums which the Contractor considers to be due to him under the Contract. Within . . . months after receipt of this final account and of all information reasonably required for its verification the Engineer shall issue a final certificate stating

(a) the amount which in his opinion is finally due under the Contract and (after giving credit to the Employer for all amounts previously paid by the Employer and for all sums to which the Employer is entitled under the Contract),

(b) the balance, if any, due from the Employer to the Contractor or from the Contractor to the Employer as the case may be. Such balance shall, subject to Clause 47 hereof, be paid to or by the Contractor as the case may require within twenty-eight days of the Certificate."

Clause 68—Notices

Employer's address ....

Engineer's address ....

Clause 70—Changes in Costs and Legislation

This Clause should cover such matters as:—

Adjustment of Contract Price, in both local and foreign currency expenditure, by reason of alteration in rates of wages and allowances payable to labour and local staff, changes in cost of materials for permanent or temporary works, or in consumable stores, fuel and power, variation in freight and insurance rates, Customs or other import duties, the operation of any law, statute, etc.; price adjustment formulae to be used, if any.

Clause 73—Taxation

Taxation—payment of or exemption from local income or other taxes both as regards the Contractor and his staff.

Clause 74 etc.—Miscellaneous (To be inserted if required)

Regulations governing importation and use of explosives for blasting; bribery and corruption; photographs of the Works and advertising; undertakings regarding non-disclosure of secret information; submissions of shipping and other documents, etc.

Conditions of Contract

PART III—CONDITIONS OF PARTICULAR APPLICATION TO DREDGING AND RECLAMATION WORK

Introduction

In Dredging and Reclamation Work the Contractor is not normally held responsible for the maintenance of the Works after takeover; the Works are usually taken over in sections as they are completed; the Contractor can only work economically if he is allowed to work continuously by day and by night; the incidence of Plant Costs (mobilisation, supply and demobilisation) forms a much higher proportion of total cost in the case of a dredging contract than is generally the case with construction contracts; as plant supplied by the Contractor almost invariably includes ships and at times includes ships taken on charter by the Contractor he cannot give to the Employer the unrestricted right to sell such plant. The Employer may find cover against the risks of non-completion by an increase of the amount of the performance bond.

Quantities included in the tender documents must necessarily be estimates the accuracy of which is inherently less than normally experienced on construction contracts.

Part III—Conditions of Particular Application to Dredging and Reclamation Work

The Conditions of Contract (International) for Works of Civil Engineering Construction shall be amended by the addition, as Part III, of the following provisions.

Part I and Part II of the Conditions

(a) References to "Constructional Plant" shall be understood to relate to all dredging and reclamation plant and appliances and all ancillary plant required for use in the execution of the Works.

(b) References to "Essential Hired Plant" shall be understood to relate to "Constructional Plant" (as defined in Parts I and III of the Conditions of Contract (International) for Works of Civil Engineering Construction) the withdrawal of which in the event of a forfeiture under Clause 63 might (having regard to the methods of construction, dredging or reclamation employed prior to the forfeiture) endanger the safety or stability of or result in serious disturbance to the execution of any part of the Works and which is held by the Contractor under any agreement for hire thereof.

(c) References to "Maintenance" and "Period of Maintenance" shall have effect only if it is agreed between the parties that the Contractor shall specifically be responsible for Maintenance of the Works or any part thereof.

Clause 5 (2)

For "Parts I and II" there shall be substituted "Parts I, II and III".

Clause 10

For "stated in the Letter of Acceptance" there shall be substituted "indicated in the Tender documents".

Clause 11

The Employer shall have made available to the Contractor with the Tender documents such data on soil specifications and hydraulic conditions as shall have been obtained by or on behalf of the Employer from investigations undertaken relevant to the Works and furthermore depending on the nature and situation of the Works such additional data necessary in connection with the execution of the Works like navigation conditions, environmental conditions, dumping places and such particular data and the Tender shall be deemed to have been based on such data, but the Contractor shall be responsible for his own interpretation thereof. The Contractor shall also be deemed to have inspected and examined the Site and its surroundings and information available in connection therewith and to have satisfied himself, so far as is practicable, before submitting his Tender, as to the form and nature thereof, but he shall not normally be called upon to satisfy himself as to the quantities of materials to be dredged more accurately than he can deduce from the Tender documents and inspection of the Site only.

Clause 12

The words ("other than climatic conditions on the Site") shall be deleted.

Clause 18

Exploratory excavation shall be deemed to include dredging.

Clause 20 (1)

Where arrangements are made for sections of the Works to be taken over as they are completed the Contractor's responsibility for any such section shall cease forthwith upon its acceptance.

Clause 20 (2)

In view of the relatively small but highly specialised labour force employed, the "excepted risks" shall include epidemic disease.

Clause 21

The Contractor's obligation to insure under this Clause shall be limited, unless otherwise specially agreed, to the insurance against normal marine risks of all Plant (including ships) supplied by the Contractor for use on the Works whether owned or taken on charter by the Contractor. Such insurance shall be effected with an insurer and in terms approved by the Employer (which approval shall not be unreasonably withheld).

Clause 40 (1)

(a) In the event of suspension of work by either the Engineer or the Employer, the extra cost to be borne by the Employer shall in case of Plant chartered by the Contractor include the bare boat charter hire of such Plant in lieu of its depreciation.

(b) The stipulation under (c) shall be deleted).

Clause 45

The Contractor shall have the option to work continuously by day and by night and on locally recognised holidays subject only to any specific restrictions stipulated in the Contract.

Clause 51

The alterations, additions and omissions (provided for in Clause 51) shall be imposed upon the Contractor only insofar as they can be executed by means of the Plant used or intended to be used in the execution of the Works as orignally specified by the Contractor in his tender documents.

Where no order has been given by the Engineer under Clause 51 (1) for the variation of any item of the Bill of Quantities and it is found on completion of the Works that the actual quantity of such item differs from the estimated quantity stated in the Bill, a variation shall be deemed to have been made by the Engineer for which no written order is required and to which the scheduled rate for that item shall apply.

For "within seven days" under Clause 51 (2) there shall be substituted "within fourteen days".

Clause 61

For "Maintenance Certificate" there shall be substituted "Final Completion Certificate".

Clause 62

For "Maintenance Certificate" there shall be substituted "Final Completion Certificate".

The Final Completion Certificate shall be issued within 14 days of completion of the Works.

Clause 63 (1)

The last sentence of this Clause commencing "and the Employer may at any time sell" shall be deleted.

Clause 63 (4)

In the case of Essential Hired Plant the Employer shall not be entitled to sell such Plant as is specified in sub-clause 63 (5).

Clause 63 (5)

With a view to securing in the event of a forfeiture under Clause 63 hereof the continued availability for the purpose of executing the Works of any Essential Hired Plant the Contractor shall not bring on to the Site any Essential Hired Plant unless the agreement for hire thereof contains a provision that the owner thereof will on request in writing made by the Employer within 7 days after the date on which any such forfeiture has become effective and on the Employer undertaking to pay all hire charges in respect thereof from such date hire such Essential Plant to the Employer on the same terms in all respects as the same was hired to the Contractor save that the Employer shall be entitled to permit the use thereof by any other contractor employed by him for the purpose of completing the Works under the terms of the said Clause 63.

Clause 63 (6)

The Contractor shall upon written request made by the Engineer (which request shall not be questioned by any arbitrator) at any time in relation to any item of Essential Hired Plant submit to the Engineer a certificate, officially certified by an Authority (e.g. notary public) to the satisfaction of the Engineer stating that the agreement for the hire thereof contains a provision in accordance with the requirements of sub-clause 63 (5).

Clause 63 (7)

In the event of the Employer entering into any agreement for hire of Essential Hired Plant pursuant to the provisions of sub-clause 63 (5) of this Clause all sums properly paid by the Employer under the provisions of any such agreement and all expenses incurred by him (including stamp duties) in entering into such agreement shall be deemed for the purpose of Clause 63 hereof to be part of the cost of completing the Works.

**SHORT DESCRIPTION
OF WORKS**

Form of Tender

(NOTES:—The Appendix forms part of the Tender.

Tenderers are required to fill up all the blank spaces in this Tender Form and Appendix.)

To:..

GENTLEMEN,

Having examined the Drawings, Conditions of Contract, Specification and Bill of Quantities for the execution of the above-named Works, we, the undersigned, offer to execute complete and maintain the whole of the said Works in conformity with the said Drawings, Conditions of Contract, Specification and Bill of Quantities for the sum of...

.... (£..............................)

or such other sums as may be ascertained in accordance with the said Conditions.

2.   We undertake if our Tender is accepted to commence the Works within...........................days of receipt of the Engineer's order to commence, and to complete and deliver the whole of the Works comprised in the Contract within...........................days calculated from the last day of the aforesaid period in which the Works are to be commenced.

3.   If our tender is accepted we will, if required, obtain the guarantee of an Insurance Company or Bank or other sureties (to be approved by you) to be jointly and severally bound with us in a sum not exceeding   per cent. of the above-named sum for the due performance of the Contract under the terms of a Bond to be approved by you.

4.   We agree to abide by this Tender for the period of...........................days from the date fixed for receiving the same and it shall remain binding upon us and may be accepted at any time before the expiration of that period.

5.   Unless and until a formal Agreement is prepared and executed this Tender, together with your written acceptance thereof, shall constitute a binding Contract between us.

6.   We understand that you are not bound to accept the lowest or any tender you may receive.

Appendix

	CLAUSE	
Amount of Bond or Guarantee (if any)	10 ( )	.... %
Minimum Amount of Third Party Insurance	23 (2)	
Period for commencement, from Engineer's order to commence	41	.... days
Time for completion	43	.... days
Amount of Liquidated Damages	47 (1)	.... per day
Limit of Liquidated Damages	47 ( )	....
Amount of Bonus (if any)	47 (3)	....
Period of Maintenance	49	.... days
Percentage for Adjustment of Provisional Sums ...	59 (4) (c)	.... per cent.
Percentage of Retention	60 ( )	.... per cent.
Limit of Retention Money	60 ( )	....
Minimum Amount of Interim Certificates	60 ( )	....
Time within which payment to be made after Certificate	60 ( )	.... days

Dated this .... day of .... 19 .... ,

Signature .... in the capacity of ....

duly authorised to sign tenders for and on behalf of ....

....

(IN BLOCK CAPITALS)

Witness ....   Address ....

Address ....

....

Occupation ....

Form of Agreement

THIS AGREEMENT made the.. day of...

19............ BETWEEN..

of ....

....(hereinafter called "the Employer") of the one part and................

....of..

....(hereinafter called "the Contractor") of the other part

WHEREAS the Employer is desirous that certain Works should be executed, viz...

....and has accepted a

Tender by the Contractor for the execution completion and maintenance of such Works NOW

THIS AGREEMENT WITNESSETH as follows:—

1. In this Agreement words and expressions shall have the same meanings as are respectively assigned to them in the Conditions of Contract hereinafter referred to.

2. The following documents shall be deemed to form and be read and construed as part of this Agreement, viz.:—
    (a) The said Tender.
    (b) The Drawings.
    (c) The Conditions of Contract (Parts I, II and III*).
    (d) The Specification.
    (e) The Bill of Quantities.
    (f) The Schedule of Rates and Prices (if any).
    (g) The Letter of Acceptance.

3. In consideration of the payments to be made by the Employer to the Contractor as hereinafter mentioned the Contractor hereby covenants with the Employer to execute complete and maintain the Works in conformity in all respects with the provisions of the Contract.

4. The Employer hereby covenants to pay the Contractor in consideration of the execution completion and maintenance of the Works the Contract Price at the times and in the manner prescribed by the Contract.

IN WITNESS whereof the parties hereto have caused their respective Common Seals to be hereunto affixed (or have hereunto set their respective hands and seals) the day and year first above written

The Common Seal of..

.... Limited

was hereunto affixed in the presence of:—

        or

SIGNED SEALED AND DELIVERED by the

said ....

....

in the presence of:—

* Delete where inapplicable.

INDEX